Body Chic

Finding new strength & vitality

Carolyn Cheshire

with Jim Lewis

TIGER BOOKS INTERNATIONAL
LONDON

Acknowledgements

I'd like to thank Julian Feinstein for all his help and encouragement throughout the years I have been body building. Without his invaluable support there would be no story to tell.

Julian has also been largely responsible for writing the text, and helping in every way to put the book together.

There are other people I would like to thank too.

Firstly, three special photographers: Jimmy Wormser who always produces such stunning pictures of me, Steve Rees who did all the studio and gym shots, and Rena Pearl for "Julie's Big Day" and her photograph of Rachel McLish.

Ben Weider, Rachel McLish and Corrina Everson for contributing to the book with such kind words.

Jim Lewis of Gold's Gym, Covent Garden, for his advice and the use of such excellent facilities.

Angela Jeffs, my editor and Sue Gell, the designer.

Photo credits

Steve Rees: Back cover; p.77 and all studio and gym photography
Jimmy Wormser: Front cover; p.13 (left); pp.22-3
Rena Pearl: pp.112-124
Bob Kennedy: pp.19,21,26,33,109
Julian Feinstein: pp.17,126
Doris J Barrileaux: p.11
Edward Hankey: p.8
Steve Douglas: p.13 (right, top and bottom)

CLB 4411
This edition published 1995 by
Tiger Books International PLC, London
© 1995 CLB Publishing, Godalming, Surrey
All rights reserved
Printed and bound in Italy
ISBN 1-85501-623-0
Text © 1985 Carolyn Cheshire and Jim Lewis

Contents

Preface 4

INTRODUCTION
How I Began Body Building 6
Why Get Started? 14
Fitness, Health and Fashion 16
Who Is It Good For? 18
Popular Myths and Facts About Body Building 19
Know Your Muscles . . . 22

STARTING OUT
All the Things You Need 24
Warming Up 26
The Home Exercises 34

JOINING A GYM
My First Visit to a Gym . . . by Jim Lewis 77
What Do I Look For and What Do I Want? 78
Using a Gym: the Exercises, the Equipment and How to Use It 80

NUTRITION AND DIET
The Dangers of a Bad Diet 102
A Balanced Diet 104
Carolyn's Diet 108
Supplements or Not? 110
Vitamin and Mineral Check 111

BODY BUILDING AS A COMPETITIVE SPORT 112
Julie's Big Day 114

Pregnancy 125

Holiday Exercises 125

Glossary 127

Index 128

Preface

Body building is now an international sport for women, as well as men. As a pioneer in her field, for she has never flinched from her unswerving belief in herself and in the beneficial effects of body building for other women, Carolyn Cheshire has achieved enormous respect from sister and brother competitors and professional bodies alike. Proof of this is the fact that, on hearing that Carolyn had written a book to encourage women into body building, not one, but three individuals came forward with their blessing, encouragement and stamp of approval. The words that follow are authoritative proof of the worth of this book and its importance to women today.

Competing onstage at the highest levels of body building competition, promoting it on television, at press conferences, giving seminars, attending movie premieres . . . The bond we share as pioneers in the sport, the lifestyle, the belief of body building as the ultimate form of physical expression is reason enough to encourage this book and others like it.

The beauty of body building lies within the goals and motivation of the individual. Whether you want to just tone up and shed excess weight or whether you have the enthusiastic desire to elevate yourself to higher levels of physical excellence, you need one thing before you begin – a good solid understanding of the basics.

Carolyn Cheshire's BODY CHIC will help you on your way.

Rachel McLish
1980/82 Miss Olympia

With more and more women interested in body building and weight training to firm up and shape their bodies, it is critically important that good instruction be made available. BODY CHIC meets that demand.

I've known Carolyn Cheshire for just a short time – two years, to be exact. However I've come to realise just how dedicated she is to her cause and mine, showing women how they can improve their physical being through progressive body building.

Working in the sport for over six years, Carolyn is more qualified than most of the people passing themselves off as exercise gurus. She's a people's champion, working to remove stereotypes from the sport, and to change our old ideas and prejudices about women. I know she's put her heart and soul into this book, just as she does in a contest. I recommend BODY CHIC to anyone who wants to move into the new world of women's body building.

Read and study what Carolyn has to say: BODY CHIC is what's happening in the world of body building right now.

Corinna Everson
1984 Miss Olympia

I have known Carolyn Cheshire since 1980 when she first entered the IFBB Miss Olympia Contest in America that year. She has competed in this prestigious contest every year since.

BODY CHIC is a rare find. It deals with the often overlooked area of starting women's body building. How to begin at home . . . how to condition yourself for effective workouts with free weights . . . how to reach your highest point of personal achievement in body building and fitness. BODY CHIC is particularly useful to the woman who has neither the time, nor money or even the inclination to train at a commercial gym. But by the same token, this book prepares you to the extent that you will be ready to train at a gymnasium should you wish to.

There is no one better qualified than Carolyn Cheshire to write the book. As a former top model she has quickly become Britain's number one woman body builder. In fact, she is Britain's *only* professional woman body builder, and ranks in the top echelon worldwide. I firmly believe that no other individual exceeds Carolyn Cheshire's knowledge on the subject of women's body building and fitness.

BODY CHIC is as competent as its author. It too is positive towards our sport; it holds back nothing and will doubtless help many thousands of women achieve physical superiority, better strength, increased fitness and more vigorous health. I fully endorse this excellent book.

Ben Weider
President
International Federation of Body Builders

Corinna Everson   Rachel McLish   Ben Weider

One from my model book

How I Began Body Building . . .

Very recently, at one of London's major body building contests, I was approached by a man of mature years who was eager to paint me. He had seen my photograph on several occasions and was attending the contest with a dual purpose in mind: to research his subject, women's body building, so as to understand it better, and in the hope of making contact with me. He succeeded in both his aims, and when I learned that the person in question was Felixs Topolski, one of our most successful contemporary artists, I was most honoured.

Felixs, for his part, was delighted when I agreed to sit for him and we arranged to meet at his studio. I was not in my very best contest shape by any means when Felixs began his work. However, he was totally enthusiastic. "You have perfect proportions," he proclaimed, "the ideal female physique".

Once again I received confirmation of just how much body building can do for women. But things were not always like that.

It seems like only yesterday that I was attending modelling school part-time. There were weeks and weeks of hard work. Learning how to walk, to turn, to stand, to smile, to apply make-up and so on, and afterwards perhaps the possibility of being invited on to the agency's books and then perhaps, perhaps, to do some modelling work. In my case however this was conditional upon my losing weight from around my waist and hips. Like many others on the course, I was a bit too pear shaped.

I was determined and by sticking to a low calorie, black coffee for breakfast type diet, achieved my goal. My measurements were on target. I had whittled away at my natural English pear shape and was ready to be a model of the Twiggy mould.

And that's the way I remained for quite a few years, as I experienced the excitement and disappointments of modelling life. The high spots included high fashion seasons on the catwalk, photographs in VOGUE and HARPERS, and appearances in the title sequences of no less than five James Bond Movies.

My boyfriend Julian had been dabbling with weight lifting and weight training for many years and seldom missed a workout at Dan Donovan's Melcombe Gym where at last his interest turned to bodybuilding. Every now and then his enthusiasm got through to me and on two occasions we travelled to Crystal Palace to witness the Skol Strongest Man contest which in those days meant strictly Olympic Lifting.

Shortly afterwards we became interested in body building. A friend of ours, Michael Andreou, competed in the Mr. Arndale contest, organised by Dave Prowse – Darth Vader of Star Wars fame – and Julian had been along to see this. There had also been a women's contest and whilst being fairly impressed, Julian had felt that I would do well if I entered the competitions.

Some months went by before I was at last persuaded to attend a contest and when I saw the women concerned, I inadvertently suggested that I was in better shape than they were. Quick as a flash I was challenged to prove the point and then there was no turning back.

I entered an old style National Amateur Body Building Association (NABBA) contest in Solent City, Portsmouth. Making the assumption that it would be judged on some kind of physical culture criteria, I exercised with a vengeance to ensure that I had no wobbly bodyfat. To my surprise this mattered little. When it came to the judging I found myself well down the field behind several fairly chubby competitors. I might have quit right there and then had it not been for a bit of encouragement by long time body building aficionado, Wag Bennett.

My next effort was at the Mr. and Miss Arndale contest just one year after Julian had first attended. Yet again I was to learn something new. This contest had some of the more successful NABBA women in the field and they produced what is called 'Continental' posing, a style of erotic pin-up posing which was fashionable in those types of contests. I found this far removed from what I had considered a sports activity. Though I finished last there was encouragement and advice from Oscar Heidenstam, the NABBA President, and his assistant Norman Hibbert, who directed me towards training with weights, albeit very light ones. They told me that I needed more meat on my upper body, which I decided to resolve. I also started to devise my own style of posing.

I won my next contest at Eastern Counties, and began working harder in the gym. Soon I was being placed regularly in local contests but felt puzzled to see some very fleshy girls in favour with the judges, particularly in the major shows.

I continued in this vein with some success, even reaching the NABBA Great Britain finals in 1980. Though my posing routine proved very popular with the crowd, a senior judge and official

believed my posing to be all wrong and my appearance far too masculine. It was, after all, a bathing beauty contest I learned. This, in my *naïveté*, astonished me and made me realise that I was headed in a different direction from my fellow competitors. As a result I cast my eyes across the Atlantic to America where women's body building was experiencing birth pangs and photographs of its exponents were beginning to be published.

George Snyder, the Philadelphia based promoter, had held a contest for women the previous year called The Best in the World. It was based on body building lines and required each contestant to demonstrate that she trained with weights by performing an exercise, namely the bench press. They had to press 60% of their body weight upwards, whilst lying on their backs on an exercise bench, for ten repetitions. This was more in line with my ideas so I started to train with heavier weights. This was essential if I was to increase my muscle size to balance my physique, and to overcome the qualifying barrier.

I saved all my money and with the help of information received from Sharon Welles of the American magazine MUSCLE DIGEST, and Kim Cassidy, the Washington promoter, I planned my US campaign, where all contests were organised by the Inter-

national Federation of Body Builders (IFBB), strong rivals to NABBA. It was to include two contests, Kim Cassidy's prestigious East Coast event, the US Nation's Capital Championships, and, if I did well enough, a week later the

The first time a London crowd had seen a female body builder, October 1980

Miss Olympia. The latter had replaced The Best in the World, and although initially it had been difficult to get my entry accepted, pictures demonstrating my development and the boost of a win in Don Styler's Solent City contest, based on a points system and which included physical development, clinched my place. Had I not fared well in Washington, though, I doubt if I would have risked exposing myself in the Miss Olympia field.

Back home I was finding that training facilities for women were few and far between, a long way from today's explosion of gyms and health studios. In fact, it was a real struggle to find places to train each week day. Finally at the eleventh hour, my luck changed. Julian's new club of a few years standing, St. George's, was a gym of the old school – old, damp, tough, rough and ready.

After applying for membership for several months with little response I finally received a reply. It was positive. I had been accepted. Good old St George's; they had given me a break. But all was not over yet. The first day I walked in I was greeted by a petition. On the notice board was a list of names supporting the motion that women members should be debarred. Fortunately good sense prevailed and the petition died a death.

Right from the start my con-scientious though naïve training, my strict low carbohydrate, high protein diet and my good proportions stood me in good stead. At the US Nations Capital contest, I took third place from an enormous field amidst an electrically charged atmosphere generated by the standing room only crowd.

Winner of this major Washington contest was top star Deborah Diana, and if I had any doubts about my affinity to women's body building, it was removed by the excitement evoked by my first ever 'posedown'. This is the last round of a contest where all six finalists are allowed to move about freely and show their best poses in direct competition with each other.

I then went on to compete in the Miss Olympia and finished a satisfying thirteenth from a very large field. Standing alongside Rachel McLish and the other top American stars made me aware of the improvements which I needed to make, as well as the extent to which it was possible to mould the physique by means of body building. I resolved that by the time the next Miss Olympia came around I would be a genuine challenger for the top spot.

But a lot was to happen before then. Exhilarated by my US experience, I returned to the UK and continued my preparations for the NABBA Miss Bikini. I had entered the previous year and had received a cool reception from the crowd. This year I would compete as a body builder.

As there were no specified criteria for physical culture contests for women, I used body building posing both at the Bikini judging and the show. Before the judging began I approached the judges and requested that the comparisons might be carried out barefooted so that proportions might more accurately be assessed. This flummoxed the judges who immediately went into conference. They reported back to me saying that whilst it was perfectly alright for me to be barefooted as I looked good without shoes, it would be unfair on the other girls.

During the judging nearly all the contestants were called for at least one comparison. Except myself that is; I was totally ignored. It was almost as if I was not part of the contest. As the judges talked freely amongst themselves, thereby destroying any independent assessment, I knew that it would only take one or two of them to say something derogatory about women's body building for the remainder to lose the confidence to contradict them.

As a tiny measure of insurance, I had one surefire supporter in the audience besides Julian. It was former junior England discus star Konrad Eberlein who had the world's loudest voice so I knew I would have at least one favourable bit of support! Fortunately his impersonation of a one-man crowd was not required, I received a tremendous reception.

I had been invited to compete in the Biggest Show in Europe in Ostend, Belgium, two weeks later. I was rather reluctant as I suspected the judging would be on a similar basis to the Bikini contest. The promoters, however, were very keen for me to compete so I made the journey across the Channel. This time the judging was live during the show. The crowd gave me, the first body building woman they had ever seen, an unbelievable reception. Later, when the results were being announced and it became apparent that I was being overlooked, several of the contestants were booed, including, unfortunately, the winner Jacqui Nubret.

This latter incident finally removed any doubts that I may have had. As my main concern was competing again in America and particularly in the Miss Olympia, I set about improving my physique and posing with this in mind: softening up my muscularity and saccharinising my posing to satisfy some officials, was incompatible with my long term aims. As I had no intention of regressing, I therefore resigned myself to withdrawing from European competition.

Just at this time, two fortuitious things happened. A poster advertising the British Federation of Body Builders Championships was displayed in St George's Gym where I was still the only female member, indicating that they were to hold the first British Women's Body Building Championships in Wales. I wrote to the organiser to confirm that IFBB women's rules would be enforced and then maintained my training with this as a new target.

Shortly afterwards the BBC contacted me because they had seen an article about me in COMPANY magazine, and wished to do something on women's body building on the Russell Harty TV Show. The idea was to compete with the Miss World Beauty Contest on the commercial channel. I gave them a considerable amount of help and to their credit, Carol Caldwell, their researcher, checked all the angles, incuding obtaining a copy of the NBC video tape of the US Women's Nationals from Atlantic City and film of the World Amateur Body Building Association's Miss World contest in Paris.

I appeared on the programme, together with Karan Thomas, and Bridget Pasquil, who represented the 'physical culture' rather than body building school. We were interviewed and later posed. The programme went very well, especially for the body

builders and Russell Harty, who was apparently hostile towards us, was won over by our attitude during rehearsal and received us sympathetically. The following morning I received a telephone call from Oscar State, who was sufficiently impressed by the way I had handled myself with Russell Harty to feel that I would make a good ambassador for body building. He asked me to stand for election for the newly formed IFBB International Women's Committee. I was later elected by the IFBB Congress in Manila.

Unfortunately the TV show served as a catalyst to bring to the surface the hostility which some of the officials felt towards us. On the morning of the show, a senior NABBA official telephoned the BBC because he was concerned about the public getting the 'wrong image' about women's contests, viz that they might be thought of as being about body building. He specifically wanted to know if I would be appearing, and when this was confirmed he made derogatory remarks to the effect that no normal man would like to go to bed with a woman such as me, that is, a body builder. He implied that neither I, nor any other body builder, should be used on the programme. The BBC spokesperson informed him that, even from her limited knowledge, the purpose of women's body building was purely sporting and not a

My first Miss Olympia, August 1980, with Rachel McLish

whenever required, and in the space of a year competed no less than thirteen times and made guest appearances on a further eight occasions. This included two visits to Holland where a lot of interest was created. German journalist, Gerd Wald, who was reporting the Bikini and Ostend contests featured my story and photographs in a German magazine. This helped create enormous interest in that country too.

My action packed year included wins in the Midlands and the English Championships, and a chance to compete again at the highest level. Not only did I finish thirteenth in the first women's World Championships, but with Angelito Lesta, finished fifth in the World Couples Championships in Atlantic City.

Unfortunately whilst in the US I sustained a painful and persistent neck injury which frustrated my training and forced me to wear a supporting collar in order to be able to sleep. This coupled with my inability to hold my body weight led to my greatest disappointment. The European Championships were my fourth contest in a month and my high metabolism and resulting loss of weight nearly took me down into the under 52kg lightweight class. (Class weight at International level is always determined in kilograms, physical weight in pounds.) I was well defined

means of enticing men into bed. I think though, that this illustrated the kind of criteria which some judges seemed to apply in 'physical culture' women's contests.

Three days after the Russell Harty Show, the British Championships were held at

Caerphilly under offical IFBB body building rules, and this proved to be the beginning of a new era.

My plans to concentrate on preparing for just one contest, the 1981 Miss Olympia, were abandoned. I did my best to promote the sport but lacked muscle density and my high hopes were shattered when I finished fourth behind Finnish sensation Kike Elomma.

But there were compensations.

Standing in the crowd at Caerphilly at those British Championships months earlier, had been the highly regarded television documentary maker, Graham Moore. For quite some time he had been wanting to make a documentary on women's body building, but lacked a suitable subject. Though I finished second, Graham seemed to have little doubt that I was Britain's best woman, and he used me as a vehicle for a major television documentary. Out of this was born "Muscle Madness", a big budget one hour programme which took women's body building seriously and tried to understand its fascination. It was favourably previewed and attracted over seven million viewers.

That was the end of the beginning. Soon after, I was forced to abandon my amateur status. The Miss Olympia, in which I participated in 1980, was designated a professional contest and when the dust settled, I found myself excluded from all amateur competition.

I retain the honour, however, of competing in all five Miss Olympia contests, a distinc-

tion only equalled by America's Lyn Conkwright. In addition, I have competed in three World Championships and two World Couples Championships. In the Couples contests, Angelito Lesta and I finished fifth and fourth in 1981 and 1982, in the teeth of fierce competition from the top American professionals. More recently Andrew Searle and I won the British Championships and, of course, there was my individual success as English Champion in 1981.

My most bitter sweet moment came at the 1983 Miss Olympia in Philadelphia, when I made great gains and took everybody by surprise. Only Carla Dunlap from America and Lisser Frost-Larsen of Denmark were in the same kind of contest condition as myself, and most observers and every single one of the body building magazines saw me finishing amongst the top few. But it was not to be. WOMEN'S PHYSIQUE PUBLICATION saw me as placing fourth, whereas FLEX, the official journal of the IFBB stated "Most observers thought she (my good self) would easily place in the top six; upon reflection it seems unfair that she did not."

In his editorial in the same magazine, Ricky Wayne, thundered "How in heavens name did Kike Elomaa (the Finnish former 1981 Miss Olympia titleholder) beat

Carolyn Cheshire . . .?" A small compensation was a Miss Olympia Special Award for the Most Improved Body Builder from the writers of MUSCLE AND FITNESS and FLEX, the two most influential American magazines.

Besides my visits to America, I have travelled around the European body building scene and always try to keep in close touch with all developments. I have received advice on training and nutrition from many sources and make a point of evaluating most carefully whatever I hear before testing out the ideas personally. Then, unless I am convinced of the value and merit of the advice, I never pass it on.

I believe that in many ways, the competitive professional body builder is like a racing driver; someone who drives a car to its very limit. Often by subjecting a car to extreme conditions, lessons are learned and these lessons can then be applied to the family saloon. In the same way by going flat out in training or in dieting, you can achieve good results in a comparatively short period of time. The same principles can then be applied less vigorously to all women.

I feel that my own success is a personal testimony to the fact that body building works. And from now on it's going to work for you too.

My most recent pictures . . .

Why Get Started?

When a new or interesting sport arrives on the scene and titillates the media, it doesn't take long before lots of people want to get involved. Some do so just for the fun, say as a hobby; others have clear goals or objectives. Sometimes these goals are achieved; in other instances they are misplaced. And whenever the latter happens disillusionment soon follows.

Take aerobics classes for instance. What a great way to get fit, and by this I mean heart-lung, or as it says, aerobic fitness. Certainly aerobics have made women fitter than ever before. Dashing up and down stairs and sprinting for the bus no longer hold terrors for aerobics regulars, who also become far more supple, achieving an elasticity they may not have experienced since their early teens.

But what of those who wish to shape their figures, to look good on the beach? I agree aerobics help, particularly at the beginning, when there are more calories being burned than usual, and the metabolism speeds up. But there tends to be a levelling off process as the body adapts and becomes used to the rigours of the class. It turns out, in the end , that aerobics classes on their own are not enough to shape and mould the figure into the athletic form of the 1980's.

Then there are women who choose to shape their bodies through diet, and diet alone. This is an effective way to remove some pounds from your frame and the results will soon show themselves on the scales. But though the successful dieter looks fine in clothing she also knows that all is not quite well underneath. Often the flesh is not of the tone or consistency desired, because dieting on its own isn't selective enough in eliminating fat. Ultimately the body adapts to the diet and retains its fat until the point is reached where lean tissue is being burned for energy. The dieter is left slimmer but often with a relatively high proportion of fat. And fat just cannot be shaped through diet.

Now let's look at body building. We should start with the fundamentals and consider what happens to the human physique when it begins to age.

From the age of about eighteen onwards, if the body is left to its own devices the muscle tissue begins to atrophy and the amount of fat stored on the human frame steadily increases. This continues until the day we finally die. Even with apparently slim people, when they reach middle age, the ratio of fatty tissue to muscle which makes up their bodies, is much higher than

when they were younger. They may even weigh exactly the same as they used to, but there the similarity ends.

In fact, it is this process – the change in the proportion of muscle to fat – which to the naked eye makes us look older. There are other contributory factors such as the elasticity of the skin but these are secondary.

So what does body building have to do with this? Well, resistance training with weights stimulates muscle growth, thereby increasing the amount of lean body tissue or muscle, while a sensible, balanced low fat diet decreases the amount of fat we store on our frame, precisely the opposite of what happens with aging.

So body building serves to keep the aging process at bay and if taken up later in life even reverses its apparent adverse effect.

The youthful physique always seems to have such a firm and attractive appearance. So often in the past it was the full young almost untrained figure which prevailed in bathing beauty contests or the 'Miss' contests which used to form a large part of competitive body building.

All too soon those youthful physiques would lose their tone only to be replaced by even fresher faces and figures. With women body builders, and by this I mean those who train with weights, this does not occur.

These women look to improve the shape of their physiques, and it's only muscle and certainly not fat which can be shaped and moulded, to improve from one year to the next.

But what, you might ask, about all the other sports?

Running or jogging must be the first which comes to mind. Certainly this is another aerobic activity, that is one which improves the fitness of the heart and lungs, making you healthier, giving you increased stamina and serving to keep weight down. What it will not do, however, is allow you to change or enhance the appearance of your physique or figure in a positive and controlled manner.

If we move on to other sports such as tennis, squash, hockey and so on, once a certain level of aerobic fitness is attained here, further improvement results only from speeding up the responses of the nervous system. By this I mean faster hand-eye co-ordination, quicker reflexes or anticipation near the tennis net, and similar changes for the better.

All these sports are good healthy challenging and fun activities, but none of them approaches the efficiency of body building in the way it affects the human physique.

Body building is no mere fad and I feel confident that the world at large is just beginning to discover the means of staying younger and looking good.

It's easy to start at home

Fitness, Health and Fashion

Isn't it amazing how much fashion dictates the way we look? Women seem to be able to contort themselves into all shapes and sizes to keep up with one trend or another. Sometimes it means squeezing into tortuous dresses, or pinching feet into vice-like shoes. On occasions it even involves changing our physical shape.

Look at any of the works of Rubens, that prolific artist of the late sixteenth and early seventeenth century. Here was a man who not only mastered the vast canvas but who is forever remembered for the voluptuous plump models he featured in his paintings. At a time when art served as a medium of entertainment every woman must have strived to achieve that pink cherubic chubbiness that Rubens so adored.

But times change and nowadays clothes can be wrapped around almost any figure. The actress of the Eighties has no difficulty in impersonating her counterpart in a Restoration Comedy. Corsets provide a handy aid to achieve that vital wasp-like waist and the right kind of support and exposure will ensure that exactly the right amount of bosom is on display.

Even in Victorian times the bust was emphasised, though more modestly exhibited, and of course, bustles were designed to draw attention to the bottom and so further exaggerate an hour-glass appearance.

In the Twenties we had the flapper girls, straight up and down, slim, rectangular and without a waist to be seen. Did everyone really look like that or did the clothes cunningly conceal the truth from our eyes?

In the Forties and Fifties, the sweater girl was our model of so-called perfection. Woollies showed plenty of bust and separation, and if someone didn't quite have all the flesh needed to fill that sweater, why then there were ways and means of fooling the eye. Ideally the bust was also underpinned by curvy shapely legs, as personified by Betty Grable, before and after the Second World War. And, if you didn't quite have Betty's legs, then a pair of finely seamed stockings and high stiletto-heeled shoes helped to create some of the illusion.

For a short while the rigours of rock and roll dancing meant dispensing with the heels, so flatties became essential. But it wasn't too long before the tall, bustless models of the Sixties took over. A glance at the fashion magazines of that era shows how ultra slim we were supposed to look and how shapeless legs seemed to be.

Shoulders appeared terribly narrow and if they weren't naturally so, then pehaps a little adjustment of the posture would help.

A medical condition, *anorexia nervosa*, reared its ugly head, and now is frequently discussed in magazines and textbooks alike. The illness, due to a psychological complaint or perhaps a mineral deficiency, which causes its victims to starve themselves as they seek an ever slimmer appearance, may have always been with us. It is just possible, however, that the extreme fashions of the day might have exacerbated matters.

The twentieth century has seen more change in style and fashion than any other era, which is hardly surprising considering the sophistication to which the various forms of media have been raised. Not only do we know what everyone in England is up to fashion-wise, but within minutes the television can inform us of all the latest trends in Paris, New York, Tokyo and everywhere else. And within weeks all the magazines follow this up in black and white and colour, giving us all the time we need to take in every detail. Fashion is now multi-cultural, with ideas stemming not only from Europe and America, but also from Africa, India and the Far East.

In recent years the medical profession has placed much emphasis on preventative medicine, the Western world's most serious killer, heart disease, receiving the lion's share of attention. The preventative steps were pretty

When I first started body building

clear: stop smoking, eat less fatty foods and take plenty of exercise. And this applied to women just as much as to men. Not only the superstars, the high school heroines of sport, the tennis players and athletes who appeared on television, but everybody – all of us.

Jogging and aerobics classes became extremely popular in the late Seventies and early Eighties, and always just one step away from the aerobics class were the weights, the Multigym and more recently the Nautilus equipment.

Many of these developments have been in response to a vast change in the thinking

among athletics and sports coaches. No longer is weight training taboo for athletes and other sports people. The long-standing fear that lifting weights will result in a sportsperson becoming muscle bound, stiff and slow, is being replaced with a new conviction that weight training is a short cut to enhancing performance. Through weight training exercises, specific muscles can be isolated, trained and strengthened and this new capacity can then be applied to the original sport.

The first prominent sportswoman that I heard of who openly admitted to training with weights was that phenomenal Australian tennis star Margaret Court (Smith), who won Wimbledon several times, and virtually every other major tennis title. She had a service of exceptional power and it's no surprise to learn that modern day cham-

pions, like Martina Navratilova, use similar methods. Most recently, in her efforts to keep pace, Chris Evert-Lloyd has also resorted to weights to give her added power.

I can recall that whilst watching a television talk show in America in 1980, Playboy's Barbara Benton, the model for the original Barbie Doll, proclaimed that she liked muscles and trained with weights, much to the consternation of her TV host. Since then it is clear that Bo Derek, Chrissie Brinkley and many many other media figures train with weights.

Most recently of all, top photographic and fashion model, Marie Helvin, the photographer David Bailey's ex-wife, has strongly advocated body building. "When I first started as a model they made me stay at around 105lbs. I looked terrible . . . Thank God the new interest in fitness and sport has changed the shape of women today . . . "I want muscle," proclaims Marie.

Yet for once this is not simply a fad, a fashion designer's whim or, as feminists claim, men's wishes. For the first time, what is fashionable coincides with what is healthy and beneficial. Looking like a body builder means more muscle and less fat. Not mere camouflage but a truly more youthful body.

Who Is It Good For?

Body building is for everyone and anybody, providing that they have no really serious medical problem. (Check first with your doctor if in any doubt.) The beauty is that you can start off from wherever your present physique happens to be and with hard work, but at a pace which suits you, make rapid progress.

With most other sports such progress is rarely publicly revealed, perhaps only on the tennis court or in the privacy of your sports hall. With body building it's different. As soon as you make progress, you will know it and as a result you will feel good and that's going to encourage you to do more and more. When your friends see you they will comment favourably. How fit and well you look they will say. And when you get onto the beach, you'll really enjoy walking around with – or depending on where you are without – your bikini! Your firm toned muscles will feel great and your confidence will rocket sky high.

About age. Besides the fact that we have had several top professionals such as Georgia Miller-Fudge and Kay Baxter competing whilst in their forties, the rejuvenating effect of body building is exactly what many mature women need to boost their egos and to put the zest back into living.

I have a pupil who is a mature woman with a highly successful business, which takes her travelling all over the country. Recently she had a serious operation, something which always has a draining effect, and although she had not participated in sports activities for years, she decided that she needed to do something to ward off the aging process.

She has thrown herself into body building, and though she struggled with lady press ups in the beginning, after only a few weeks, she was doing three lots of twelve full scale press ups. She feels really good about herself and has already noticed how much less fatiguing she finds her work, besides being delighted at how much smaller and firmer her waist has become.

She is a great example of what can be done with three or four hours training per week, at home, with only the simplest pieces of equipment.

There is an experiment which will be familiar to all those readers who know their flea training! And if the analogy escapes you for the moment, all will soon become clear.

If you put some fleas in a jar we all know exactly what will happen. Fleas are good at one thing and that's jumping, and in no time at all they will have leaped out of the jar and gone on their way. So if we want to keep them there it's a good idea to put a piece of cardboard over the top of the jar. The fleas will at first leap up and bang their heads on the cardboard, but very soon they'll get the idea that if they don't jump quite so high then they will avoid getting hurt. So the fleas will keep jumping because that's the sport they're good at, but they'll stop just short of the cardboard.

Now here's a strange thing. We can take the cardboard away and the fleas will still not leap out of the jar. Even though they have the potential to escape whenever they want to, they stay in the jar. They have put an imaginary ceiling on their ability. Many people do exactly the same.

There are two ways to get a flea out of that jar. The first way is to put a new flea into the same situation. The new arrival doesn't know anything about the cardboard. It simply glances round, thinks what on earth are we all doing here, promptly leaps out and goes on its way. The others look at each other and say "Did you see that?" Then they all follow suit and in no time at all they're off.

The other way to get the fleas out of the jar is to put a bunsen burner underneath!

Well, I'd like all the readers of this book to get rid of their imaginary bits of cardboard. Your body building is going to make you like that new flea who knows no boundaries. It is going to help you shrug off living for evermore with Aunty Celia's big hips or worrying about being a little too old. And maybe, just maybe, I'll be a little bit like that bunsen burner encouraging you on your way.

This is where it can lead you

Popular Myths and Facts about Body Building

Many women have preconceived ideas about body building, some based on fact, others a complete fiction. Let me clear up some of these anxieties before we go any further into the subject.

1. "Body building will make me muscle bound and I'll lose flexibility."

Women who have larger than average muscles gained from heavy weight training are more flexible than the average person, because their training emphasises using their muscles against a resistant force through the complete range of movement for every repetition. This brings about an improvement in joint and muscle flexibility when the muscles are free to move without the resistance or weight being present.

2. "Body building will make me look masculine."

Do I look masculine (or does Rachel McLish)? A woman will always have small muscles and less strength than a man, because a woman has greater quantities of the female hormone oestrogen and less of the male – muscle building – hormone testosterone. All that can truly be shaped is muscle, whether it be on the male or female body. This means that the gains in muscle mass will enhance your shape, thereby increasing femininity, and creating curves which may have been previously hidden beneath layers of fat.

3. "I don't want to get big muscles in my arms."

This is the common fear of most women when they start training. Indeed it was one of my own anxieties, an attitude which was reinforced by instructors where I trained, who discouraged me from training my arms. "Women," they decreed, "just do not do those exercises." But big arms are really difficult to obtain. Body builders train round the clock, sweating blood to get big arms, and if anyone finds the formula for obtaining big muscles overnight, they'll become a millionaire! No, increase in size is achieved slowly, because of the low levels of testosterone in a woman's body, and there is no danger of waking up one morning and finding that you have huge arms!

4. "Body building will slow me down."

Not so. Athletes in nearly every sport use weight training to increase their strength and speed. Sebastian Coe and Steve Ovett, both athletic world record holders, use weights as an integral part of their training. Top tennis players, such as Chris Evert-Lloyd and Martina Navratilova, also recognise that weight training is essential to keep themselves at a peak of strength and fitness for gruelling tournaments.

5. "I'll lose my bust if I do bench pressing."

I've often wondered where this old wive's tale originated. It seems to circulate in gyms and crops up fairly regularly. Let me reassure you that you will not loose your bust through bench pressing. Quite the opposite. The muscles you'll develop, the pectorals, help support the bust and keep it looking firm and youthful. As the bust is fatty tissue, if you are overweight and go on a diet, you will lose fat from your bust as well as your waist, hips and bottom. This is perfectly logical, but has got nothing to do with the bench press, which will in fact build you up.

The bench press is a very

popular and effective body building exercise which we will discuss in depth later on. Being a more advanced exercise requiring gym equipment, it's not one of those which you will be doing early on whilst at home, but it is one of the first exercises that you will see people doing when you walk into a gym.

6. "Eating a grapefruit before a meal will burn fat."

Another myth without any foundation. No amount of grapefruit, nor any other fruit, will burn fat. Grapefruit are useful as a part of a diet, because they are very low in calories. They are also filling, and as they are on the sour side without being unpleasant, they help to retrain your taste buds, weaning them away from sweet foods to sharper ones. Finally, of course, grapefruit are a rich source of Vitamin C – so they have lots of valuable properties, but not as a magical fat burner.

7. "If I eat meat that takes a lot of chewing, I must be eating fibre."

It is not fibre but the sinews of a tough cut of meat that are exercising your jaws. Dietary fibre (or roughage) is found in fruit, vegetables and grains and is essential for proper digestion and eliminating constipation as well as more serious disorders. Good old fashioned porridge oats are an excellent source of soluble

fibre (yes, mother really did know best!).

8. "Squatting will give me a big bottom."

It's fat that gives you a big bottom. Squats performed correctly (i.e. feet shoulder-width apart and heels raised on a 1 in-1½in block, and then bending the knees to a deep squatting position before pushing upwards, using the thigh muscles and not the back) will not only firm and tone the front thigh muscles but also the gluteus maximus (or bottom) muscles. These are the largest muscles in the body.

9. "My thighs will become huge and out of proportion as soon as I start training them using weights."

All that happens is that the newly formed muscle will push the still present fat outwards. As the combination of exercise and diet burn away the fat, your shapely legs will be revealed underneath.

10. "My muscles will turn to flab when I stop exercising."

Muscle and fat are two different tissues – muscle cannot turn into fat and fat cannot turn into muscle. If you stop exercising you have to reduce the amount of calories you eat, or the surplus calories not used up by the exercises will be stored as fat. It's all a matter of balancing energy (food) intake with energy expenditure.

11. "It's possible to sweat unwanted fat away."

I'm afraid this is not so. When you perspire heavily in a sauna or plastic wrap, you are merely ridding your body of water, which will be replaced as soon as you drink fluids.

12. "It's possible to get rid of excess fat with massage."

No amount of pummelling, thumping, bottom banging or massaging will make fat go away. Only the combination of a reduced calorie intake and exercise will achieve the reduction of stored body fat. Remember, it's been around for a long time so will take longer to get rid of initially, but once it has gone, then it becomes easier to keep your figure fat free.

13. "Pregnant women should not lift weights."

As I explain in more detail later in the book, sensible and careful weight training can only be of benefit during pregnancy. Stronger shoulders and backs are needed to support larger, heavier breasts, and stronger abdominal muscles mean a shorter labour, an easier delivery and a quicker recovery.

14. "When on a diet, cheese and salad make a good balanced meal."

If you are trying to lose body fat, then it's certainly not a good idea to eat a hard cheese like Cheddar. For every 3½oz, Cheddar cheese is 33% fat, 25.5% protein, and contains a whopping 397 calories. Cottage cheese is more virtuous, as per 3½oz it contains only 4% fat, 13.6% protein and 96 calories! Mixed with a salad (no dressing is required when using cottage cheese), it makes a well balanced slimmer's meal.

15. "Training with heavy weights will make my periods stop and bring on premature menopause."

It's not only women body builders who worry about *amenorrhea* (loss of periods), but also athletes, ballet dancers, marathon runners and so on, all of whom tend to be very lean and carry very little body fat. A doctor who has researched the subject extensively, Dr Joan Ullyot, reports that it is only because we have all become more plump and inactive through modern day living, that periods are nowadays a regular phenomenon. In times gone by when we were all nomadic and lived as hunter-gatherers and therefore had to keep moving, women would have been leaner and very much more active. Menstruating regularly in those times would have slowed our progress, and allowed flesh-eating wild animals to track us

down. Body builders have low body fat and are simply reverting to a more basic and natural pattern which is much more appropriate to healthy women. As soon as you ease off heavy training (after a contest for example) and allow your body fat levels to increase slightly, your periods will soon be reactivated. Be warned though, *amenorrhea* cannnot be regarded as being a contraceptive substitute.

When all the myths are behind you!

KNOW YOUR MUSCLES . . .

I will be describing in the following pages how you can develop certain muscles in your body. Use these annotated photographs to identify your own.

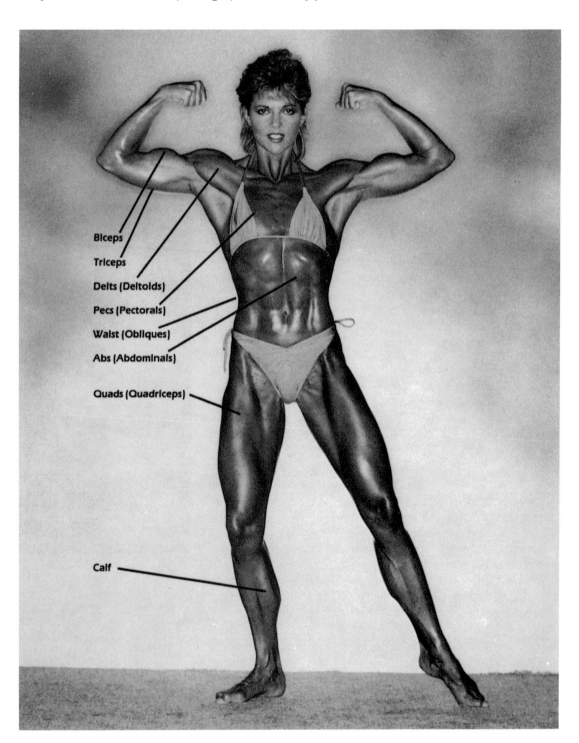

Biceps

Triceps

Delts (Deltoids)

Pecs (Pectorals)

Waist (Obliques)

Abs (Abdominals)

Quads (Quadriceps)

Calf

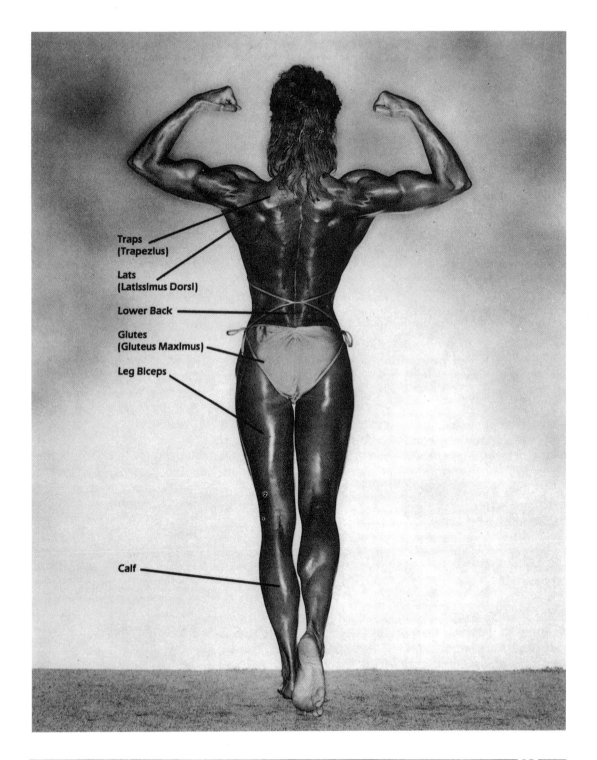

Traps
(Trapezius)

Lats
(Latissimus Dorsi)

Lower Back

Glutes
(Gluteus Maximus)

Leg Biceps

Calf

Starting Out

Now we are ready to begin body building. But before you begin you need to prepare yourself.

ALL THE THINGS YOU NEED

Let's assume that you are going to be starting from scratch right there in your home. First, get organised.

1. You will need enough clear carpeted floor space to allow you to stretch out and twist round without being hampered. It's also vital that the carpet is secure and not likely to slip or slide, otherwise you could injure yourself.

2. Make sure that the room is reasonably warm. Exercising in a freezing cold environment is another way to invite strains, or even worse damage, torn muscles.

3. Reasonable ventilation is also vital. Body building means the expenditure of energy and since oxygen is the medium we use to burn fuel for energy, make sure that the room is not too stuffy.

4. The first bit of equipment that you need is a firm and stable kitchen chair.

5. Somewhere at home you are sure to have a heavy stable bit of furniture. You will need this to support you when you do sit up exercises for your abdominal muscles. If necessary, this could be in another room.

6. Steal some firm large cushions from your three – piece suite or better still find some floor cushions or very firm pillows. If you don't have any cushions then I'll suggest later on how you will be able to improvise using the corner of your bed.

7. In addition one small cushion will be useful.

8. Buy a broom handle from your local hardware shop. A 4ft length will be fine and shouldn't cost much.

9. Fish out a thick telephone directory or a catalogue about 1½in thick. Better still, get hold of a fairly large piece of wood about 2ft long, about 8in-10in deep and about 1½in thick. If it is a little larger, no matter.

10. Now for the real equipment, starting off with a pair of dumbells. I recommend that you purchase a pair of 5lb rods and collars plus four sets of 1½lb weights (or plates as they are known), and four sets each of 3lb plates and 5lb plates. This is a most economical purchase because body building is all about progressive resistance training or steadily increasing the amount of weight you use, thereby providing the muscles with the opportunity of doing more. In principle the more weight that the muscles have to handle, the more they will develop. This statement is broadly accurate, though there is always a point at which we reach our individual limits. Otherwise we could all just go on lifting bigger and bigger poundage.

11. It's always worth asking around because it's amazing the number of people who have old sets of plastic dumbells lying about. If you can get hold of a pair of these, or even a single dumbell, there will always be a use for it.

Don't be put off by the heavier ones. I remember when I first started, I was given a gift of two 3kg dumbells. "Oh no, these are all wrong," I cried, "they are much too heavy; I wanted the ladybells of 1½kg or 3.3lbs each." Fortunately I was persuaded that I would soon grow into using the 'biggies' and I have to admit that I did.

12. Purchase a pair of ankle weights of roughly 3lbs each. Now in this case please don't go for heavier ones in the belief that you will grow into them. The 3lb pair will be quite enough.

13. Ultimately you will need a training belt as you advance, but in the case of anyone who gets twinges in their back, it would be advisable to buy a belt early on. Make sure it fits you and that it can be tightened if you are planning to lose some weight, or will expand by at least one notch if you are planning on building up.

14. Last but not least, you may be wondering what you should wear. Rule number one is to be sure that whatever it is, it doesn't restrict your movements. Shorts with a T-shirt or tank top, together with training shoes, are fine for most purposes. Alternatively leotards or the type of outfits worn by aerobics class devotees will also fit the bill. If your room is a little on the cool side then you might want to wear a light sweater or a tracksuit until you are warmed up. However, a sweater wrapped round the waist, which some people regard as fashionable, is superfluous in most instances. As far as a bra is concerned, this depends on your figure and the type of support your bust requires. In most instances the answer is probably "yes" just to be on the safe side.

A leotard is comfortable for training

Warming Up

The main reason for warming up is to avoid strains and injuries. These can easily result if you throw yourself straight into a tough exercise. Warming up is exactly what it sounds like. It's about encouraging the circulation of blood to warm up the body, gently stretching the muscles to ease away stiffness. The warm up should be conducted at a brisk pace and should take no more than about five minutes.

1. Start with some gentle jogging and speed up as you begin to loosen up.

2. Bend over at the waist whilst keeping your legs straight and allowing your arms to hang freely. Then try gently, but as firmly as possible, to push your head towards your knees. Next reach forwards and backwards in a controlled manner about 10 times. Finally straighten up.

FORWARD

Let's get going

BACK

3. Keeping your legs straight place your feet about 18in apart. Bend over again at the waist and using both hands twist and reach as far as possible towards your right foot. Then relax and repeat, reaching down to your left foot. Do several reptitions.

4. Stand straight, feet together. Now look upward and reach up, until your right hand is stretched as high above your head as possible. Attempt to reach even higher. Now switch to your left arm. Repeat several times.

5. Raise both arms straight above your head with fingers interlocked, and place your right foot about 18in behind your left. Now arch backwards in a controlled manner achieving a good stretch. Do the same with your left foot placed behind the right one. Repeat several times.

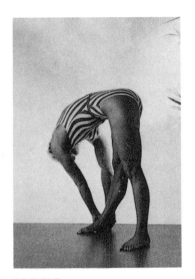

TO RIGHT

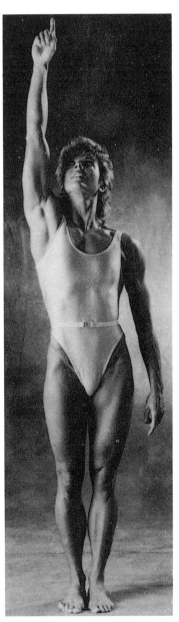

LEFT LEG

TO LEFT

RIGHT ARM

6. Now raise both arms straight above your head and stretch as high as you can. Bend over keeping your legs straight and reach down with both hands to grasp your ankles – or get as close to the ankles as you can manage! Pull very gently 9-10 times.

7. Stand upright with your feet slightly apart. Raise your elbows until they are parallel to the floor and pointing out to either side. With your feet firmly anchored, twist at the waist from side to side 20 times.

TWIST RIGHT

START

TWIST LEFT

8. Stand upright with your hands placed low on your hips and your legs fairly wide apart. Then bend your right leg and push your hip out. Do the same with your left leg and hip and repeat 10 times.

9. Stand with feet about 2ft apart. Bend over and grasp your legs as close to your ankles as you possibly can. In a similar way to the previous exercise, push your right hip out to the side to stretch the inside of your thighs, and then repeat to the left side. Do this exercise 10 times.

TO RIGHT

TO LEFT

RIGHT LEG

LEFT LEG

10. Stand upright, making sure you are comfortably balanced. Raise your right knee off the ground as high as you can. Grasp that knee with both hands and pull it towards you, almost hugging it. Do the same with your left knee. Repeat several times.

11. Stand upright with your hands at your sides. Tilt your head gently towards your right shoulder. Try not to jerk. Bring your head back to an upright position and then tilt it towards your left shoulder and back to an upright position. Gently tilt it backwards in a controlled manner and then allow your head to come forwards so that your chin touches your chest. Repeat about 4 times.

BACK

FORWARDS

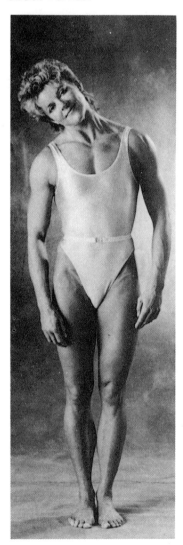

TO RIGHT

12. After completing the previous exercise, gently rotate your head through all the same positions as described, but, in a continuous motion and without returning in each case to the upright position. Rotate once in a clockwise direction and once in an anti-clockwise direction.

13. Stand upright with your arms at your sides. Rotate or shrug your shoulders. Firstly rotate them forwards, up, backwards, down and repeat, and then reverse the direction. That is, rotate them backwards, then up, forwards, down and finally return to the starting position. Repeat several times.

BACK

UP

FORWARDS

14. Lastly, sit on the floor with your legs apart and stretched out in front of you. Lift both arms in front of you until they are parallel to the floor. Stretch your arms forwards as far as you can, trying to touch your feet. If you can't touch your feet, don't worry; just stretch as far forwards as you can manage comfortably. Return to a more upright position and then stretch forwards again. Repeat 10 times.

START

MIDPOINT

FINISH

Now on to the real work!

Exercising at Home

If you don't have suitable cushions for exercises such as flyes, dumbell presses and so on, you can improvise by using the corner of a divan bed. Lay with your head in one of the corners at the foot of the bed and your legs placed diagonally across. This allows your elbows to overlap the corner of the bed and gives you a bit of extra stretch whilst you do your home exercises.

SHOULDERS

Several factors contribute to the athletic bearing that is currently so fashionable. A slim waist is one of them, but so is a broad-shouldered up-right stance. Athletes always seem to have a good pair of shoulders on them.

In some cases our genetics have blessed us with exactly those requirements, good shoulders and a slim waist. If so, we can use body building to enhance those assets; if not we are going to use all our know-how to create that very illusion. Because, if you develop your back and shoulders and trim whatever is possible off the waist, this creates that magical taper. Then, lo and behold, every-one will be saying how lucky you are to have such a good natural shape!

There are other benefits. Shoulders which slope exces-sively, i.e. from either side of the neck towards the arms, are not always attractive. Nor are very narrow shoulders and, least of all, round or hunched shoulders, which tend to make the neck disappear.

Sometimes these problems are inherited through our genes, but often they stem from bad habits. At one time, in the Sixties, it was fashion-able for teenage girls to assume a hunched posture, and once started these habits tend to remain. Similarly tall girls who are self-conscious of their height when they are young often round their shoulders so as to be less conspicuous. But this is no disguise and round shoulders usually stay for life.

It's only through body building that we can make real changes, improving on nature as well as all the bad habits I have just described. With today's fashions, parti-cularly in summertime, the shoulders are highly visible; they can be seen from every angle. So that's the way we will train them – to look good from all sides.

ALTERNATE DUMBELL PRESSES

These first two exercises are to work and strengthen all your shoulder muscles.

Pick up your set of dumbell rods, which will weigh around 5lbs, one in each hand, and hold them at shoulder level. Standing upright with your back straight, push your right hand overhead until your arm has straightened or 'locked out', and then lower it again to the shoulder in a controlled manner. In fact both move-ments should be done in a controlled manner and under no circumstances should the dumbells flop down to the shoulder during the second part of the exercise. Repeat this movement with your left arm. Do 10 repetitions.

RIGHT ARM

LEFT ARM

If this proves to be too easy then you might want to add the 1½lb or 3lb plates to the bar to increase the level of difficulty. However, make your judgement as to how easy or difficult it is after doing all 10 reps with each arm, not before.

You can do three sets of 10 reps (3 × 10) with this exer-cise, gradually increasing the weight as you become stron-ger, and resting for no longer than 20 seconds between each set. After you have been working away for say six or seven weeks you should increase the weight progres-sively after completing each set. For instance, you might start with the rods alone. The second set might be done with the rods plus two 1½lb plates on each dumbell sec-ured by the collars, making a total of 8lbs for each dumbell. The third set might be heavier again. Use the 3lb plates with the rods, so that each dumbell weighs 11lbs.

When you start your pro-gramme the weight you use will be dictated by your strength, fitness and degree of natural aptitude. The beauty of this is that you will make progress regardless of your starting point and that you will get there in the end. And believe me, you'll soon see some exciting changes.

These principles are funda-mental to body building and progressive resistance training and apply to all the exercises in your schedule.

DUMBELL PRESSES

A variation on alternate dumbells presses is to press both dumbells overhead simul-taneously. Most people find this exercise marginally more difficult than alternate presses. For this reason it's better to start with the alternate presses and then move on.

Pick up your set of dumbell rods and lift them to your shoulders. Under complete control press them both overhead until your arms lock out. Then lower your arms back to the start position. Repeat for 10 reps. Follow the same principles for increasing the weight as described for alternate dumbell presses.

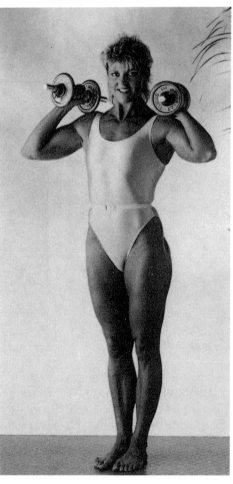

START

FINISH

LATERAL RAISES (OR SIDE RAISES)

This is the first of three exercises for the deltoids (delts), those caps on either side of the shoulder. The pro-gramme is designed to develop them from every angle and will help those of you who have particularly narrow shoulders to gain some extra width.

Pick up your dumbell rods and stand upright, your arms at your sides with your palms facing inwards. With your elbows just slightly bent and keeping your palms facing down, raise your arms until your hands are at, or nearly at, shoulder level. Hold them there for the count of two and lower them. Ideally you should try to lower them slowly and under complete control, but this may prove too difficult to start with. Repeat for 2 × 10 reps.

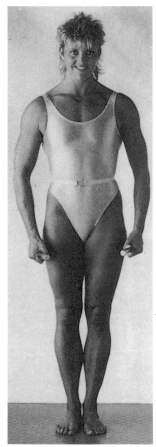

START

FINISH

At the beginning, some of you may find this exercise too tough to do with the rods. In this case, imagine you are holding imaginary rods and using just your hands do the same movement under strict control. You will soon be able to use the rods.

FRONT RAISES

Stand upright holding the dumbell rods in either hand. This time extend your arms in front of you with your palms facing towards the front of your thighs and your knuckles facing away from you.

Keeping your back straight and still, raise the rods in front of you until they are well above your shoulders and at an angle of about 45° above your head as you straighten your arms. Count to two and

then lower your arms back to your starting position in front of your thighs. Repeat for 10 reps; then do one more set.

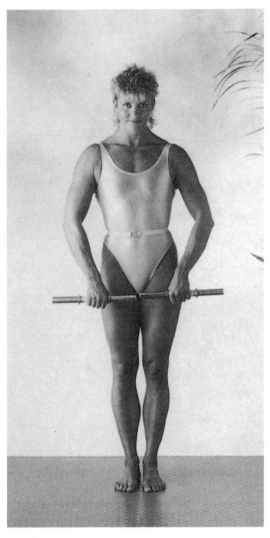

START

FINISH

This is another exercise which may prove difficult at the beginning. If this is the case, it would be sensible to

do the exercise in correct style, with imaginary rods, until you improve the movement. Gradually you will build

up a little more strength and can then move on to the rods.

BENT OVER RAISES

Grasp the dumbell rods in either hand and bend forwards allowing your knees to bend slightly as well. Your trunk should be parallel to the floor, with your arms hanging down at either side. Bend your elbows slightly and make sure your hands are well clear of the floor. Your palms should be facing towards each other a shoulder width apart, with the knuckles pointing outwards. When you are comfortably balanced, raise your arms outwards until they are outstretched in a line which is more or less parallel to the floor. Hold for a count of two and lower; repeat for 2 × 10.

START

FINISH

Remember all the usual principles about increasing the weight. In this instance, make the dumbells up to 8lbs each by adding the 1½lbs plates, and then when you can manage it, increase them to 11lbs each by adding the 3lbs plates and so on. Avoid resting for any longer than 20 seconds between sets for maximum effect.

■ UPRIGHT ROWS ■

This exercise develops the delts and the trapezius muscles (traps).

I used to do 'cleans', the first part of an Olympic Weight Lift called the 'clean and jerk'. This is a cracking power movement and is very popular with weight lifters, but it does take a lot of technique and practice. So nowadays I recommend something fairly similar, upright rows.

Hold the dumbell rods in either hand in front of your body, with your palms facing your thighs. Keep your hands about 9in apart during the exercise. Pull the dumbells up to the level of your chin, keeping your back straight throughout the movement. Lower them back to the starting position and repeat for 2 × 10 repetitions.

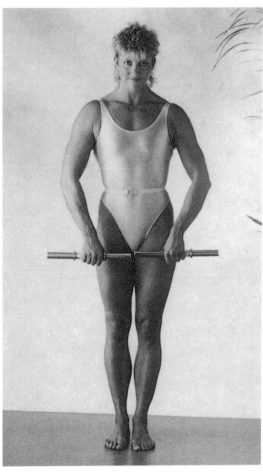

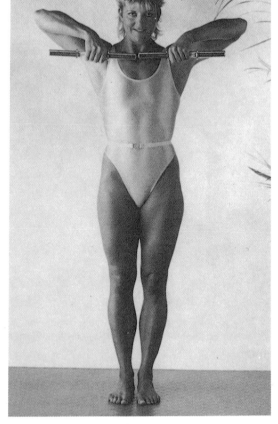

START

FINISH

SHRUGS

This last shoulder exercise is specifically for the traps. These muscles lie between the delts and the neck and they continue round the top of your back to almost meet at the top of the spine.

Besides the cosmetic effect, this exercise will help you to carry shopping and all sorts of other bags and goods which can normally be so fatiguing. (Don't worry, there is no chance of your ending up with odd looking coathanger-style shoulders!)

If you are used to carrying things, start off by picking up a set of 11lb dumbells, that is the rods with 3lb plates added on either side. Hold the dumbells in either hand with your arms at your sides, palms facing inwards.

Without bending your elbows too much rotate your shoulders towards the front, then upwards so that your shoulders almost touch your ears. Hold for a count of two, circle the shoulders towards your back and then down to the start position. Repeat for 10 reps.

Do one more set, adding weight on to the dumbells if not too strenuous. For variation you can rotate your shoulders in the opposite direction.

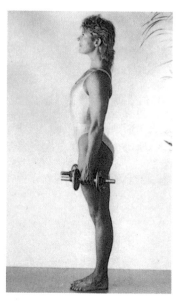

START

UP AND BACK

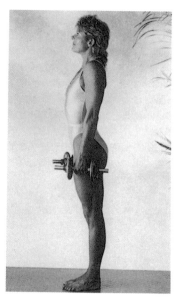

BACK

A day or two after completing your first few shoulder exercises, you will propably find that you have some aches, soreness or stiffness round the shoulder and neck area. Don't worry about this too much. It just shows that the exercises are working.

Next time round make sure you warm up thoroughly before getting stuck in. Under no circumstances should you experience any sharp pain whilst doing an exercise. If this happens when you start the programme, discontinue any exercise which causes that kind of discomfort and arrange to see a physiotherapist. It means that you're nursing an injury and physiotherapists are usually the most skilled people at diagnosing the precise location and cause of such injury and prescribing the best treatment.

PECTORALS

One of my strongest points in the first round of a professional body building contest, called 'the compulsory', is the side chest pose. But it hasn't always been like that! In fact, it was because of my pectoral muscles that I started weight training in the first place

I had entered a few physical culture contests with indifferent results: I was told that my upper body did not have enough bulk. There's only one way to correct this, and that's with weights, so I started 'pumping iron'.

Since the bust is fatty tissue which on its own can't be shaped or formed, the only thing which can be done is to build or strengthen its support. So, if you want to have a firm, high, bust-line you have to train with weights to tone and build up a web of muscles across your chest.

Many women also need to build themselves up in order to improve their proportions. A friend in her early thirties was so skinny in her upper body, though not in her thighs and buttocks, that she wouldn't wear any off-shoulder dresses or bare swimsuits. She preferred to keep herself covered, even on the beach.

She asked my advice; of course she had no intention of competing, but a programme of weight training made such a significant difference that after only three times a week for three of four months she had regained all her old confidence. Her body was in really good shape, a lovely consistent line that looked marvellous with (or without!) any clothes.

The pectoral muscles are actually very powerful and capable of doing a great deal of work. In bygone days they were used with the leg muscles when great loads had to be pushed, often uphill, as you can see in contemporary works of art. (They are, of course, always prominent on athletes' bodies.) These days most people do little strenuous work, and the muscles have tended to atrophy. If you want to change, you'll have to train to stimulate them. But remember not to exceed the three times a week schedule given on page 74.

Of course, the average woman doesn't use these muscles at all, so when weight training begins, two things happen. Firstly the muscles become sore, the kind of soreness which you might get in the calves when you jog or walk long distances after a break. The soreness is nothing to worry about as long as it isn't too severe. In fact, it only shows that the exercise has worked.

◼ LADY PRESS-UPS ◼

This exercise is widely known, and is familiar to all sorts of people. You may even wonder quite what it has to do with weight training. Well, it's essentially weight training, only instead of separate weights, you are working with the weight of your own body.

Start off by lying face down on the floor. Place the hands about 2ft-3ft feet apart in a comfortable position. Your arms should be at right angles to your body with your elbows in the air and your hands on the floor. Then push down on your palms and press your body up with your knees, remaining on the floor until your arms have straightened out. Then lower your trunk, keeping your back straight, until your chin touches the floor and then press up again. Aim at doing 10 repetitions. This is a set.

START

Once you can do these, repeat it for two or more sets, resting no more than half a minute between each set. So all in all you will have done 30 press-ups, or three sets of 10 reps. Try to increase the number of reps in a set gradually to 25, until you can manage 3 × 25.

As soon as you have got to grips with this, you can move on to do full press-ups. This should not take too long, but, because we are all different, the length of time involved will inevitably vary. Don't worry and don't rush things. It depends on whether your arms and chest muscles are naturally weak or strong, or whether you have built up some reserves through sport or heavy work.

The length of your arms is another factor. If they are

FINISH

long, press-ups are slightly more difficult because you are asking your pectoral muscles to move your body weight further. Finally, of course, there's the weight of your body. I am afraid that the heavier it is, the tougher the press-ups become. But never mind, all it needs is a bit of determination and I guarantee that you'll get there, and probably within a couple of months.

FULL PRESS-UPS

The only difference between full press-ups and lady press-ups is that instead of using your knees as the fulcrum or pivot for the exercise, you will be using you toes.

When you switch from lady press-ups to full press-ups this little trick might help to boost your confidence. Put a small cushion between your hands and under your chin. Instead of lowering your chin all the way to the floor, you will just touch the cushion. Once you can do this for about 10 - 15 reps, it's time to take the cushion away and to do full press-ups.

By this time you will be well on your way to developing your pectorals and, once you master the press-up, you will not only be that much stronger, you will have learned a very versatile body building exercise, with all sorts of variations.

START

To exercise the pectorals from different angles, vary the direction in which the hands are pointing. Keep your hands resting on the floor while your feet are on a chair. This incline exercises the upper part of the pectoral muscles.

START

For even more effectiveness, support yourself on three firm chairs. This allows you to lower your body even further; the pectoral muscles get stretched more, and as result you have to lift your body even further than for normal press-ups.

But these are tough exercises to put by for a little later on.

In the meantime there's a whole programme to accompany the press-ups and to help you achieve exciting progress.

FLYING DUMBELL PRESSES

For these exercises you'll need some large firm cushions around 2ft × 2ft square and a set of dumbells. The first exercise is almost the reverse of press-ups – you are pressing upwards rather than against the floor.

Put the cushions down in a row and lay them facing upwards. Check the illustration, and make sure your head and back are properly supported. Grasp the dumbell in either hand with your palms facing away from you and begin by resting them on your shoulders. Then slowly, and with complete control, press the dumbells upwards until your arms are locked. Lower the dumbells to your shoulders and repeat. Do 10 repetitions and increase this to 3 × 10 reps once the movement is easy. In the pictures, I am using dumbell minibars, which can weigh as much as 5lbs each. Very soon you will be able to handle this kind of weight easily, and as soon as you can add weight to the dumbells. Your first increase might be the addition of 1¼lb weights to either side of the dumbell, increasing the weight to 7½lbs.

START

FINISH

DUMBELL FLYES

This is a similar exercise which develops a different part of the pectorals. Grasp the dumbells in exactly the same way as the presses, but once you have pressed upwards and straightened out your arms, rotate your hands so that your palms face inwards and towards each other. Then, allowing your elbows to bend slightly, lower your arms in a controlled arc, stretching the pectoral muscles. Reverse the movement, pushing up in the same arc, but don't allow the dumbells to touch. Do 10 reps and increase steadily to 3 × 10. As soon as you can manage one set of 10 reps comfortably, increase the weight in exactly the same way as in the dumbell presses.

START

START

MIDPOINT

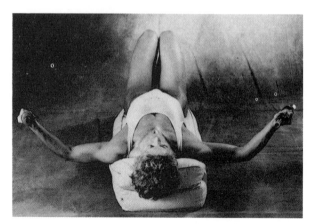

FINISH

DUMBELL PULLOVER

Lie on the cushion as described and grasp a single dumbell with both hands. Start by holding the dumbell above you and then steadily lower it behind your head. Then lift it back to the original position whilst keeping your arms stretched out. Use your whole arm in this movement and avoid any excessive jerkiness or use of your elbows. Your arms should remain fairly straight throughout; hips should be well down. This is a most important exercise as it will help thicken the upper pectorals to keep your bust high and youthful. Once again, use the same formula of 10 reps, expanding to 3 × 10 and increasing the weight whenever possible.

START

FINISH

ARMS

I remember when I first went into a gym and explored the possibility of training with weights. The first thought which came to my mind was "I don't want to get muscles in my arms".

How often I have heard those words or something similar. Almost everytime a newcomer finds herself graduating from keep-fit, aerobics or dance into the weights room, these are the fears I hear most expressed. Yet what kind of arms do we want?

As mentioned earlier, it's only muscle, not fat, which can be shaped. Fat itself is formless and unpleasing to the eye. Naturally we all carry some fat, but providing it's not predominent we can all see the shape of the muscle lying underneath.

Even a relatively small amount of fat can hide small and underdeveloped muscles. It is for this reason that a diet on its own often produces such disappointing results. Through dieting we lose both muscle and fat, rather than fat alone, and in the end we have scrawny muscles and still a proportion of shapeless fat.

We need weight training to build up the muscles whilst we diet off the fat to give us

that super end result — the sleek, chic lines we desire.

So when it comes to arms, surely all of these principles apply. But arms, and particularly the triceps area, are a problem for women. It is here that fat gets deposited and stored, often detracting from an otherwise pleasant physique.

Since I started body building I have become an arm watcher. When watching TV or a movie, I often take notice of the condition of the arms of the female stars and starlets, and in many cases they leave a lot to be desired. On the other hand women who sprint regularly have really shapely arms, which in turn is not surprising, because they all train with weights these days.

What about the professional women body builders? Whenever you see pictures of them flexing they seem to have large muscular arms full of detail. I can hear some of you saying now "I don't want to walk around with arms like that."

My answer is you don't have to. Those pictures are almost invariably taken at the time of a contest when the pro's are

at their peak and when their arms are pumped and flexed. But when they walk around the hotel lobby, in a state of relaxation, their arms look aesthetically pleasing, arms anyone would be proud of.

Take Mary Roberts or Carla Dunlap at contest, two real arm merchants! When you see them offstage you only get a hint of the explosion that's going to occur when the judging begins.

In any case, newcomers to women's body building seldom realise the effort that is required in order to develop really powerful muscles in the arms. A few sets of curls with dumbells requiring a little above average effort will not result in a pair of arms like professional body builders. In fact anyone who finds a formula to make arms without intensive training will make a fortune.

Originally my own arms were very slim and I had to pulverise them, particularly my triceps, which at one time were a weakness. Since then I've made plenty of gains and as my arms continue to develop there can be little doubt that there's some method in my madness.

■ CURLS

This first exercise is for the biceps muscles on the front of the upper arm – the ones most people show if asked to 'make a muscle'. Strangely enough it's the smaller of the two major muscle groups on the upper arm.

Stand upright gripping the dumbell rods in either hand. Your arms should be at your sides with your palms facing forwards, and your elbows ever so slightly bent. Keeping your back straight curl the dumbells in a controlled manner in a semi-circle to the shoulders and then slowly lower them again to your sides. Repeat 15 – 20 times, until you feel the muscles warm up as a result of the increased blood flow to the area. Take a rest, breaking for about 20 seconds and then repeat. If the weight feels too light then make the dumbells heavier, though I would be surprised if you find the exercise that easy to start with, providing you're doing it properly.

START   **FINISH**

Remember not to cheat or swing the curl upwards by means of swaying your body or using your back. This defeats the whole purpose of exercising the arms. When you become more advanced then there are occasions when cheating can be used to advantage, but for the present concentrate on doing the exercises in strict style. And this means lowering the weight in a slow controlled manner. If the arm is allowed to drop like a stone then you're only doing half the exercise. The lowering or negative part of the exercise is very beneficial indeed and will greatly help you to develop and progress in the most economical way.

ALTERNATE CURLS

This is a variation on the curls and it allows you to concentrate on one arm at a time.

Begin in exactly the same way as for the curl, following exactly the same principles. Curl the dumbell being held in your right hand first and then lower it; repeat the motion with the dumbell in your left hand, before moving on to the left arm and so on. This is the correct way to do the exercise and not, as can occasionally be observed in some gyms, curling the dumbells at 90 miles per hour with both arms moving like pistons!

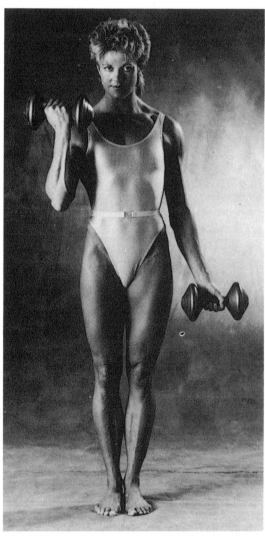

RIGHT ARM

LEFT ARM

▪ BEHIND THE NECK DUMBELL PRESS ▪

A form of what is sometimes called the 'French' press, this is the first exercise for the triceps. As I have mentioned this the largest muscle group on the upper arm, forming a horseshoe shape on the back of the arm. This is an area where women are prone to deposit fat so needless to say the horseshoe is seldom seen. I can't guarantee a sharply defined horseshoe on each arm, but undoubtedly you will achieve beautifully firm arms unblemished by excess body fat.

Place the 1½lb plates and collars on one dumbell, which will therefore weigh 8lbs. Make sure the collars are firmly fixed. Lift up the single dumbell with both hands, and place your thumbs and the palms of your hands under one plate to firmly support it. Hold the dumbell in that position above your head before lowering it very carefully behind your head, mainly by means of bending your elbows, whilst keeping them pointed towards the ceiling. Then raise the dumbell upwards by straightening out your arms before lowering it behind your neck for a second time and so on. Do 10 reps. Rest for 30 seconds and then do a second set.

START

FINISH

If at any time you feel that your arms are becoming substantially weaker and you doubt your ability to do another rep, then stop, even if it is someway short of completing the set. If this should happen whilst the dumbell is behind your neck and you can't press it upwards, then if the worst comes to the worst, let it fall behind you and step away rather rapidly. If possible, choose a spot where the least damage will result. This is one of the few exercises where it's wise to have someone around who can take the dumbell from you swiftly if it suddenly proves necessary.

BEHIND THE NECK DUMBELL PRESS (SINGLE ARM)

This is similar in principle to the last exercise, the only difference being that it's performed one arm at a time.

To start with, grasp a single dumbell rod in your right hand. Hold it above your head and then lower it behind your head, being careful not to strike yourself. Keep your left hand at the ready in case you suddenly need support and assistance. Then press your arm upwards again mainly through straightening up at the elbow. Do 10 reps. Repeat the exercise using your left arm.

START

FINISH

■ KICK BACKS ■

Try this exercise firstly without using any weights. Lean forwards slightly, bending your knees and holding your upper body more or less parallel to the floor. What is most important is that your right upper arm is parallel to the floor with your elbow bent, so that your hand almost touches your shoulder. Make a fist with your hand. Then without moving your upper arm, straighten out your arm fairly sharply (or kick it back) at the elbow until the whole arm is parallel to the floor and extended backwards. Hold for a count of two and then lower your fist slowly to the starting position. Carry on for 10 reps. Then repeat the process with your left arm. When you have the feel of this movement, then do the exercise whilst holding a dumbell rod.

START

FINISH

■ REVERSE DIPS

Before attempting this exercise wait until you have trained your triceps for about four weeks, even more if you are developing slowly. Bring in the kitchen chair and make sure that it's standing firmly. By that I mean that there's no possibility of it wobbling or slipping over.

Crouch over the seat of the chair gripping it on either side (of the seat), without letting your bottom touch, then move your feet about 18in or so away from the chair. Lower your body by bending your elbows and initially your knees as far as you can go. To begin with allow your bottom to go just past the level of the seat. Then push upwards with your arms until they straighten out. Carefully lower yourself again and repeat for 10 reps. Rest for 20 seconds; then do another set.

START

FINISH

As your triceps become stronger, you will be able to dip lower until your upper arms are parallel to the floor. In addition, instead of your knees being bent with your feet flat on the ground, you'll be able to stretch out your legs straight in front of you so that only your heels touch the ground.

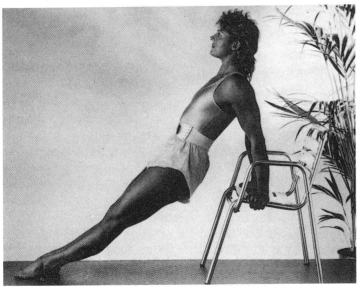

START

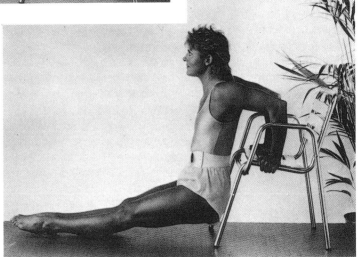

FINISH

As with all the exercises, do the triceps dips in a controlled manner, increasing the level of difficulty only as you progress and find that what you are currently doing is relatively easy. Until you become used to doing the reverse dips this is another exercise where it would be helpful to have someone standing by, just in case.

ABDOMINALS

One of the things that we nearly all yearn after is a flat firm stomach and a tiny waistline. It's the first thing that comes to mind when anybody thinks of a slim figure. And of course it's what millions upon millions of women diet to achieve.

But there are quite a few myths associated with the process of achieving such a desirable goal. The first of these surrounds diet. Without some form of diet it's highly unlikely that you will get that tiny waistline, assuming that you are carrying some flab around your mid-section before you begin your quest. However, diet on its own will not provide that firm flat toned waistline that most women would like to have. Certainly dieting will give you a small mid-section, but it will still have a fair amount of fat hanging around, and horror of horrors, below the navel your tummy might still sag!

Men usually carry fat around their waistline from where it often is the last place to go. Women however, hold their fat more readily on the buttocks, hips and thighs, as well as on the back of the arms. Unfortunately, without exercise it's just not possible to achieve that healthy toned appearance around the stomach area.

A few years ago, when I started body building, it was highly unusual for women to have defined abdominal muscles (abs). In fact there was pointed comment in some magazines which seemed to suggest that this was almost unnatural. The odd picture which showed women with visible abs were stared at with incredulity. But all this went by the board when I arrived in the US in 1980. My own abs were beginning to peep through and many of the competitors in Washington had spectacular mid-sections. And when it came to the Miss Olympia in Philadelphia a week later,

those washboard abs were two a penny.

Fortunately my own abdominals have proved to be one of my strongest body parts and I seldom devote more than 20 minutes training to them at any session.

Basically the abs can be divided into upper and lower sections and they both need to be trained. The lower abs require particular attention in the case of women, because they can sag and protrude, often ruining an otherwise quite reasonable figure.

One view is that this is natural and something that we should accept. What nonsense. Besides being unattractive, it's unhealthy and probably a result of poor posture and muscle tone. Fortunately with a bit of effort, it's a problem that is quite easy to rectify.

LEG RAISES

Leg raises firm up the lower abs. They are ideal for the beginner and extremely easy to do at home.

Lie on your back with your feet together. Lift both legs off the floor and slowly raise them, until they are about 60° to the floor and keeping the abs under tension, then slowly lower them until they are about 6in from the floor before raising them as before. Your back should be com-pletely flat on the floor, without any arching, and your knees should be just slightly bent.

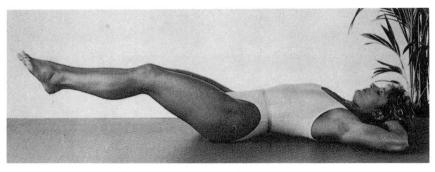

START

FINISH

The last two points are de-signed to take the strain off the lower back, which can be highly vulnerable to injury when ab exercises are incor-rectly performed.

You may struggle to do more than a few reps initially. But aim to build up to about 20 or more repetitions for each of four sets. This will soon flatten the lower abdominals.

LEG RAISES 2

When this exercise becomes easy to perform, it's time to use the ankle weights. The added resistance will make the leg raises much more difficult, so to start with set your target at 3 × 10.

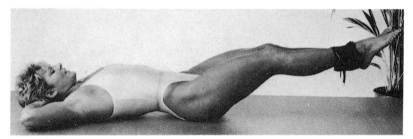

MIDPOINT

SIT-UPS

For the upper abs there's the well known sit-ups with the feet anchored under that firm piece of furniture.

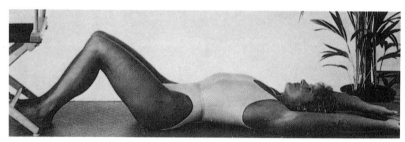

START

With your knees well bent, lift your trunk up from the floor and bring your head forwards until it touches your knees. Then lower your body until your back is resting on the floor again.

Use your arms to help lift your body to start with, swinging them forwards as you lift off the floor. Eventually this will prove unnecessary, and the entire exercise can be done comfortably with your hands held behind your head.

FINISH

Please remember to round your back a little whilst raising and lowering your body. As with the lower abs exercises, build up to 4 × 20 repetitions.

TWISTS

This next exercise is great for shaping your waistline. You can tackle it by using a broomstick or something similar.

Twists are performed whilst seated or standing. Hold the broomstick behind your neck and with your arms stretched out on either side, wrap them over the broomstick. Then without moving your hips, twist sharply from side to side. Aim to build up slowly and surely to at least 4 × 100 repetitions.

TWIST RIGHT

The one exercise to avoid at all costs is side-bends. This builds up the oblique muscles at the sides of the waist, broadening it and giving it a decidedly unaesthetic appearance. Only if I were very long and narrow in the waist would I think about doing side-bends and even then I would hesitate before using heavy weights.

It always surprises me when I see beginners in the gym doing set after set of side-bends, imagining that it will result in a nicely toned and shaped waistline. Quite the contrary, but it's amazing how popular they are.

LEGS AND GLUTES (BOTTOM)

The legs and glutes are closely linked and although there are one or two exercises which hit the glutes rather than the legs, such as the variation on hyperextensions, mostly they are difficult to separate. What we can do relatively easily though, is to separate the front of the thigh or the quads, from the back of the legs or leg bicep and glutes, and in their turn from the calves.

My attitude toward legs has changed considerably over the years. When I was a teenager I used to hate my calves which I thought were a bit on the large size and envied those skinny models who seemed to have no calves at all. My calves in fact were relatively tiny at the time compared to their size now, which is hardly surprising as I use weights of over 400lbs in an effort to train them to become even larger. On the professional circuit there are few competitors with whom I would swap calves.

However from your point of view shapely calves are an essential part of a good pair of legs, whether they be for strolling on the beach, parading in a short skirt or suit or summer shorts, or competing in a body building contest.

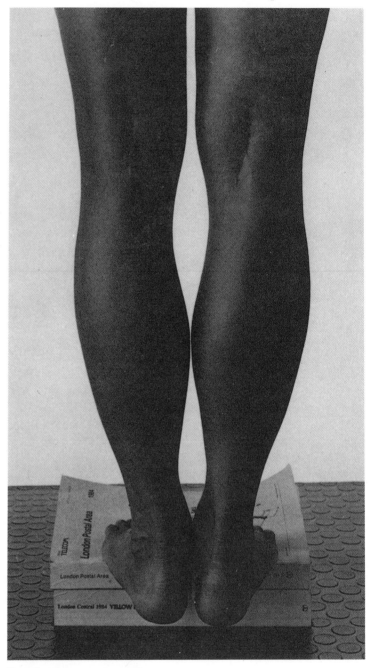

Shapely calves are your goal

CALF RAISES

The two calf exercises that follow are easy to do and they are both highly effective.

Bring out that block of wood or catalogue for this very straightforward exercise. It's probably advisable to have the kitchen chair standing nearby as well. If all else fails then you can use the bottom step of your stairs, assuming you have a staircase.

Stand on your toes with your heels about 6in apart. Your heels should overlap the edge of either the wood block, catalogue or step, depending on which one you are using. Lower your heels as far as possible and then raise them on tiptoe as high as you can get. Count up to two and then lower them again and repeat. Do 10 reps and then repeat the whole exercise again but this time with your toes pointing inwards. Do one final set with your toes pointed outwards. As you progress you may increase the number of repetitions going up to 25. Also increase the number of sets, firstly to two for each of the three foot movements and eventually to three sets for each.

START

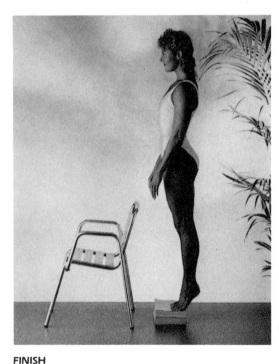

FINISH

In the early stages you may find it necessary just to touch the chair or the banister to keep your balance. You will find that your calves are really quite strong – after all they have to carry you everywhere you walk or run! Soon you may decide to increase the difficulty by holding a dumbell in each hand. Given you reach this stage you probably will require at least 15lb dumbells, that is the rods with 5lbs on each side, and maybe even more, say 21lbs. This means adding two 3lb plates to each of your 15lb dumbells.

TOUCHING YOUR TOES

An exercise to give your calves a really good stretch. Simply touch your toes with-out bending your knees, whilst standing with your back against a wall. Touch your toes 10-15 times for two sets after doing the calf raises.

Really feel that stretch in your calves

I have never stopped learning things about my thighs or quads and glutes. Before I began body building I had already accepted the idea that unless I subjected myself to the most demanding of diets then I would be pear-shaped forever, with heavy and even occasionally crêpey thighs and a big wide bottom. Body building has taught me what a load of nonsense this is. Strangely enough it has also revised my idea about the basic shape that most of us tend to assume we will have for life!

As the majority of women lead fairly sedentary lives it means that even the slimmest carry quite a high ratio of fat to lean muscle tissue. And since the first place that fat deposits itself in a woman is on the hips, bottom and upper thighs, it's hardly surprising that our expectation is that we are all doomed to be somewhat broad about the backside. However, when body builders peel off their excess body fat, it is quite extraordinary how many uncover slim-hipped boyish figures, and I don't mean only the odd one or two, but more like 25% of those in competition.

I always used to regard myself as being somewhat stout in the leg so it's strange how through training I have now come to accept that my legs are long and require a lot of work to build them up.

Which takes me back to my earliest experience of training hard with weights. Doing some squatting exercises, I was busily using a leg press machine stacked as heavily as I could manage in those days, when disaster seemed to strike! I noticed that my legs had blown up, and far from being better shaped, which was what I had been training for, they seemed to be bigger than ever. As a result I abandoned training my legs seriously for nearly six months and wasted an awful lot of time.

All that had happened was that my quads had responded to training and started to grow, but as the layer of fat had not yet diminished, what I was seeing was the newly developed muscle pushing the still present fat outwards. Foolish girl! Had I known better I would have trained even harder, taken off the cocoon of body fat and found the pair of shapely athletic legs hiding away underneath.

As it was I stopped training, took off the body fat anyway and found a pair of skinny legs waiting for me. I have been building that pair up ever since and mainly with free squats.

SQUATS

This exercise is the best one to start building up your legs.

Stand with your feet about a foot apart with your toes pointing slightly outwards. Hold your arms out in front of your body to help you keep your balance. Lower yourself down into a squat position with your thighs at least parallel to the floor. Then concentrating on making sure it's your thighs which are doing the work, stand upright again. Do 10 reps and repeat for second set. As you progress increase this to 3 × 15 reps. If keeping your hands in front of you is insufficient to enable you to keep your balance then bring that kitchen chair into play again. Just a touch on the chair should prove enough.

START

COMPLETION

If you are still having a little difficulty in keeping your balance, or perhaps finding the movement a little awkward, then a support under your heels may help. A plank of wood about ¾in thick or something similar will probably do the trick.

■ SQUATS WITH DUMBELLS ■

When the free squatting which you have just been reading about becomes too easy, then do the same exercise with dumbells.

Squat in exactly the same way as before, only hold two dumbells at your sides. You will find yourself fairly well balanced in this position.

Start off holding two 15lb dumbells and make sure that they don't touch the floor, even when you are in the squatting position. Test your-self initially with 2 × 10 reps. Then use your discretion to build up to 3 × 20.

START

COMPLETION

Once you are comfortable with squatting, occasionally (about once every third work-out) introduce a variation into your routine. Do the exercise with your feet close together, only an inch or so apart and with your knees pointing forward. This will develop your quads in a slightly different way. You will probably notice a new ache in your legs a day or so later to prove the point.

So at last we come to the leg biceps and glutes or the bottom line of body building. Whereas over the years I have heard many negative comments, usually from people who didn't understand about body builders' arms being too large, muscles being a turn off and so on, nothing like this ever happens when the discussion focuses on a set of firm muscular glutes. Then it's mainly envy. Even the male body builders draw favourable comments on these points. At a recent contest in London two good friends of mine, Pat and Theresa, were helping in the box office. Neither were by any means interested in the sport but both came in to watch the proceedings out of curiosity. One thing immediately struck both of them after seeing many-time London Champion Noris McLeod in action: "Did you see his gluteus maximus?"; "Wasn't his posterior just great!", they enthused – or words to very similar effect!

I suspect that a few of you may well have turned to this section first, so let's look now at just what we can do for your bottom and the backs of your thighs.

■ STIFF LEGGED DEADLIFTS ■

In the same way that hyper-extensions help the glutes, as well as the lower back, so these deadlifts also help the lower back, besides firming up the leg biceps and stretching the glutes.

To start with, simply practice touching your toes without bending your knees. Once you can do this and find little difficulty in doing 20 reps, then stand on your block of wood or catalogue and do the same exercise whilst holding a dumbell in each hand. Do this slowly and under complete control; under no circumstances plunge forward with the dumbells. Your hands should still reach as far as your toes because by standing on a block you can lower the dumbells beyond your feet.

START

FINISH

Start with two 8lb dumbells, though I suspect that you may soon find this too easy. If this proves to be the case, keep increasing the weight of your dumbells until they reach 21lbs or even 24lbs, the maximum that you can take with your dumbells. Of course it's always possible to buy additional plates, say 7½lbs or 10lbs or whatever you wish, whenever you decide that you are ready for more. Incidentally, this is one of the exercises in which you might use your body building belt for lower back support. Make sure that it's placed firmly around your waist, otherwise it will serve little purpose.

STANDING LEG CURLS

Grip your chair firmly with both hands. Lift your right leg off the floor and bending your knee curl it backwards, towards your bottom, lifting your heel as high as possible.

At the highest point count to two, tense your bottom, and then lower your leg. Repeat with your left leg. Continue until you have done 3 × 6 reps for each leg. Later as you

strengthen this area, switch to doing 10 reps, one after the other, for the right leg and then, without resting, 10 reps for the left leg and so on.

RIGHT LEG

LEFT LEG

Finally, when you feel that you are making substantial progress, it's time to strap on your 3lb ankle weights and go for 3 × 10 reps with each leg yet again.

WITH ANKLE WEIGHTS

KNEELING LEG CURLS

This follows exactly the same principles as the standing leg curls only this time kneel on the floor and support yourself with your hands.

Follow the same progressive path, that is, initially doing 3 × 6 reps, alternatively with back and leg. Then as you advance, switch to 3 × 10 successive reps with each leg, culminating with the use of ankle weights.

RIGHT LEG

LEFT LEG

PARTIAL WRESTLER'S BRIDGE

This little exercise is directed right at the heart of the glutes and is an excellent supplement to all the previous leg bicep and glute work.

Lie on your back with your arms at your sides and your knees bent so that your feet are flat on the ground. Using your head and the back of your shoulders to support you on one side and your feet on the other, lift your hips as high as you can, and at the same time, clench your bottom. Lower your buttocks to the floor and repeat for 3 × 10 reps.

START

FINISH

INNER THIGH FIRMER

There are two additional areas of the thigh that body builders shape and which some individuals find troublesome. These are the inner and outer parts of the thigh known as the adductor and abductor areas.

To achieve the nice overall well-shaped leg these muscles can give you, lie on your left side supported by your left arm. Raise your right leg into the air until it is angled at about 60° from the floor, then lower it. Repeat for 10 reps. Now roll on to your right side and repeat for a further 10 reps. Again, aim for 3 sets.

START

The exercise can be increased in its effectiveness by adding your ankle weights, but please don't attempt this until the movement is well controlled and easy to do.

COMPLETION

A final variation consists in supporting yourself firmly on the ground and lifting both legs into the air at an angle of 60° to the floor. Apply the same principles as before and eventually increase the level of difficulty by adding your ankle weights.

BACK

Some time ago I was a guest on the "Cat Show" which Janet Street-Porter hosted late Friday nights on television. This was an all-women programme which addressed itself to different issues each week.

The one I participated in discussed appearance and as I was to be sitting in the front row, representing body building, it was suggested that I should wear a leotard or something similar to reveal my arms, shoulders and back.

At the reception afterwards, several people who were sitting behind me, complimented me on my back and asked for a little advice on training. Whether you're a body builder or not, a shapely back and shoulders always look sexy and with today's fashions, attention is focussed often on these all-important areas.

There is an even more practical reason for training and developing the back and that is, to avoid all those niggling back injuries which are often grouped under headings such as a 'bad back', or some years ago 'deck chair back'. Both are popular terms used to cover a compendium of pains in the much neglected lower back area.

GOOD MORNINGS

So let's start with an exercise for exactly this area.

Stand upright, take your broom handle and position it behind your neck and across your shoulders. Hold it in position by placing your hands on either side of it. Keeping your legs and back straight, lean forwards slowly and steadily from the waist until your upper body is parallel to the floor. Then slowly straighten up until you are standing erect again. Repeat this for 2 × 10 reps.

COMPLETION

If at the beginning you find it too difficult to reach the parallel position then go as far as you comfortably can and gradually work towards reaching your goal over several training sessions.

SINGLE ARM ROWS

This exercise is for the lateral muscles at the side of the back, to help you appear to taper into a tiny waist.

Load 1½lb plates on to one of your dumbells, a total of 8lbs in all. Take it in your right hand and stand beside your firm kitchen chair.

Place your left hand on the chair so that you are bent over, with your dumbell arm stretching towards the floor but just not quite touching it.

Make sure that your feet are wide apart in a comfortable position and that you are well anchored. Pull up the dumbell to the side of your chest, but without moving your other hand from the chair. Repeat for 10 reps and then do the same for the left arm. Do one more set.

START

FINISH

HYPEREXTENSIONS

This is another good exercise for the lower back, helping to strengthen an area prone to aches and pains.

Lie face forward on the floor. Put your hands behind your head and lift your head and trunk upwards as high as possible. Arch your back as much as you can. Hold for a second and then slowly lower your trunk to the floor and do 10 reps. Repeat for one more set.

Should this exercise become too easy then there are two alternatives: either raise the number of reps to 15 or hold one of the 3lb or 5lb plates, behind your head.

There is yet another angle to this most useful exercise. Once the movement feels controlled and comfortable, you can use it to help firm up the buttocks or glutes. As you arch upwards simultaneously clench your bottom and continue to do so as you hold for a second, before returning to a horizontal position.

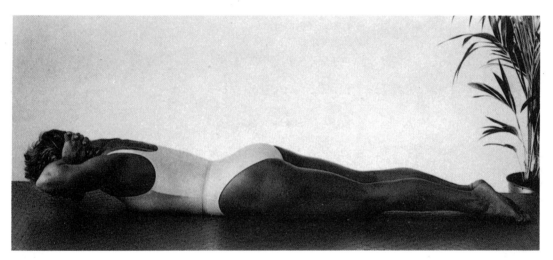

START

FINISH

SUGGESTED SCHEDULES FOR EXERCISING AT HOME

Here are three exercise schedules that I have worked out for you to follow. They have been designed to allow you to gradually build up strength and fitness, so move on from one to two to three exactly as recommended. Once the third schedule feels easy and comfortable, make this the basis of your regular workout, and then think seriously about moving on to joining a gym.

Warm up first for a total of 5 – 7 minutes.

Suggested first schedule – follow this for three weeks.
Train three times a week, e.g. Monday, Wednesday, Friday.

Body part	Exercise	Sets Reps
Chest	1. Lady press-ups	1 × 10
	2. Flyes	1 × 10
	3. Dumbell pullovers	1 × 10
Shoulders (Do exercise Nos. 1 & 2 **OR** Nos. 3 & 4)	1. Seated alternate dumbell press	1 × 10 (each arm)
	2. Front raises	1 × 10
	3. Upright rows	1 × 10
	4. Shrugs	1 × 10
Arms	1. Behind neck dumbell press	1 × 10
	2. Kick backs	1 × 10 (each arm)
	3. Alternative biceps curls	1 × 10 (each arm)
Back (Do exercise No. 1 **OR** 2)	1. Good mornings	1 × 10
	2. Hyperextensions	1 × 10
Abdominals / **Waist**	1. Twists	1 × 40
	2. Sit-ups	1 × 15-20
	3. Leg raises	1 × 15-20
Front Thigh (Do exercises Nos. 1, 4, 6 **OR** Nos. 1, 5, 3 **OR** Nos. 1, 2, 4)	1. Squats	1 × 10
	2. Stiff legged deadlift	1 × 10
	3. Leg raises – lying on side	1 × 10 (each side)
Back Thigh / **Glutes**	4. Standing leg curls	1 × 6 (each leg)
	5. Leg curls on floor	1 × 6 (each leg)
	6. Partial wrestler's bridge	1 × 10
Calves	1. Calf raises	1 × 10 (each foot position)

Schedule 2 – follow this for three weeks. Begin by warming up as usual.

Body part	Exercise	Sets Reps
Chest (Do exercise Nos. 1, 2, 4 **OR** Nos. 4, 5)	1. Press-ups (full) 2. Flyes 3. Lying dumbell presses 4. Dumbell pullover	1 × 10 2 × 10 1 × 10 2 × 10
Shoulders (Do exercise Nos. 1, 2, 3 **OR** Nos. 4, 5)	1. Seated alternate dumbell presses 2. Front raises 3. Lateral raises 4. Upright rows 5. Shrugs	 2 × 10 (each arm) 2 × 10 1 × 10 2 × 10 2 × 10
Arms	1. Behind neck dumbell press 2. Kick backs 3. Alternative bicep curls	2 × 10 2 × 10 (each arm) 2 × 10 (each arm)
Back	1. Good mornings 2. Hyperextensions	2 × 10 2 × 10
Abdominals / **Waist**	1. Twists 2. Sit-ups 3. Leg raises	2 × 40 2 × 20 2 × 20
Front Thigh (Do exercise Nos. 1, 4, 6 **OR** Nos. 1, 5, 3 **OR** Nos. 1, 2, 4) **Back Thigh/** **Glutes**	1. Squats 2. Stiff legged deadlift 3. Leg raises – lying on side 4. Standing leg curls 5. Leg curls – on floor 6. Partial wrestler's bridge	2 × 10 2 × 10 2 × 10 (each side) 2 × 10 (each side) 2 × 10 2 × 10
Calves	1. Calf raises	2 × 10-12 (3 foot positions)

Schedule 3 – warm up as usual.

Body part	Exercise	Sets Reps
Chest (Do exercise Nos. 1, 2, 4 **OR** Nos. 2, 3, 4)	1. Press-ups 2. Flyes 3. Lying dumbell presses 4. Dumbell pullover	3 × 10 3 × 10 2 × 10 3 × 10
Shoulders (Do exercise Nos. 1, 2, 3 **OR** Nos. 4, 5, 6)	1. Seated alternate dumbell press 2. Front raises 3. Lateral raises 4. Bent over raises 5. Upright rows 6. Shrugs	 3 × 10 (each arm) 3 × 10 2 × 10 1 × 10 3 × 10 3 × 10
Arms (Do exercise Nos. 1, 2, 5 **OR** Nos. 3, 4, 5)	1. Behind neck dumbell press 2. Kick backs 3. Behind neck single arm dumbell press 4. Reverse dips 5. Bicep curls	3 × 10 3 × 10 (each arm) 1-2 × 10 (each arm) 1-2 × 10 3 × 10
Back (Do exercise Nos. 1, 2 **OR** Nos. 3, 4)	1. Good mornings 2. Single arm row 3. Hyperextensions 4. Bent over rows	3 × 10 2-3 × 10 (each arm) 3 × 10 2-3 × 10
Abdominals	1. Twists 2. Sit-ups 3. Leg raises	3 × 50 3 × 20 3 × 20
Front Thighs (Do exercises Nos. 1, 4, 6 **OR** Nos. 1, 5, 3 **OR** Nos. 1, 2, 4)	1. Squats 2. Stiff legged deadlifts 3. Leg raises – lying on side 4. Standing leg curls 5. Leg curls – on floor 6. Partial wrestler's bridge	3 × 15 3 × 10 3 × 10 (each side) 3 × 10 (each leg) 3 × 10 (each leg) 3 × 10-12 (3 positions)
Calves	1. Calf raises 2. Touching toes	3 × 10 3 × 10

Joining a Gym

Carolyn works out regularly at Gold's Gym in London. The licensee and operator of this legendary Californian-based training ground for body builders is Jim Lewis. Here he explains the advantages of joining a good gym and outlines what you should look for in terms of facilities and coaching, as well as offering any number of useful hints and tips on technique and safety for the enthusiastic beginner.

Jim Lewis of Gold's Gym

Going to a Gym for the First Time

I remember when I first walked into a gymnasium weighing a measly 160lbs. It was an old basement and I was confronted with a monstrous looking man who seemed to me to be 7ft tall and 7ft across, and weighing at least 250lbs. Little did I realise then that those first few steps and that meeting would totally change my entire outlook on life. No longer the days when I would sit on the beach and have sand kicked in my face!

Having set myself this target and overcome my subconscious inhibitions about entering a gym, I found that my initial impressions of the instructor were totally unfounded. He was, in fact, keen to help me achieve my goal by constant encouragement and advice throughout the early stages.

In those days it was very much a male-orientated environment – women were not encouraged to partake of the sport; indeed many people felt that the only possible result of a woman training with weights, would be a musclebound woman. Modern techniques and machinery mean that the physique of a person who is training can be very much preconceived, so that nowadays both men and women can set themselves the goal of improving their general appearance without creating a world full of Mr, Miss or Ms Universes.

The gyms in those days, although basic in terms of facilities, were the foundation for producing the first champions of the sport, and when I consider some of the facilities available in the gyms of today, and see people entering for the first time, I reflect upon my initial reactions, and have warm affection for that first body building muscleman who introduced me to the sport.

WHAT DO I LOOK FOR, AND WHAT DO I WANT?

Having plucked up the courage to enter a gym for the first time, it's important to decide what you want to achieve, whether it be a championship physique or just the reshaping of your body to a more pleasing appearance – becoming fitter and stronger.

Remember, not everyone who jogs in the park on a Sunday afternoon aspires to breaking a world record!

What To Look For

When choosing a gym, you should always try to find the best equipped. But what do we mean by this?

A good gymnasium should have a combination of machines and free weights. By machines I mean that they should have a mixture of pulley machines where the weights are of variable resistance, each machine design-ed to exercise a specific body part. These types of machines are ideal for body building by both men and women and are normally found in most well-equipped gymnasiums.

There are various other machines on the market today which in their own way are suitable for exercis-ing; these are an additional benefit to be found in many gyms. These machines are, however, by no means vital to your progression in the sport, indeed it's far more essential that you are able to make use of the comprehen-sive range of free weights in your gym. These will be of two types, either dumbells or barbells, ranging from about 5lbs to 140lbs. Free weights are essential in that they allow complete freedom of movement, so giving greater scope in any exercise. As your body building progresses your requirements in terms of equipment will expand with your development.

Cost alone should never be the over-riding factor. In the same way as you would test drive a car, you should 'test drive' your gym before sign-ing up for a membership. Look to the equipment, the instruction and the atmos-phere, because body build-ing is 1% inspiration and 99% perspiration. To make a suc-cess of it you must enjoy your training to the full.

Instruction

There should always be competent and experienced instruction available. This is vital at the beginner's stage in order to start off on the right foot, so to speak.

Atmosphere

This is an indefinable quality that should hit you when you walk into the gym – you will know it when you find it!

Set aside a regular time to work out. Most gymnasiums have peak hours, usually in the early evening, so if it's at all possible, try to avoid this time of day. Obviously, though, your training time will be governed by many different factors.

It would be very nice if every body builder could train in one of the more than 200 Gold's Gym facilities world-wide, but not everyone has access to such good equip-ment and coaching. Gold's Gym has now been at the forefront of international body building for two decades, and has become known as the Mecca of body building. Virtually every body building superstar has at some time trained exclusively at Gold's Gym or worked out there periodically.

For most aspiring body builders, however, there may be no alternative than to work out at home in your garage or basement with only an adjustable barbell and dumbell set and a couple of benches. In the early stages, whether you train at home or in a gym, provided you train regularly and to your maximum capacity, you will make progress; but if you wish to develop your interest in the sport further it will soon become essential to attend a gymnasium and get really expert tuition.

Safety Procedures

Whilst body building is a sport with an excellent record of safety, it's vital that whether you are training in a gym or at home you must take into account the guidelines set out below.

1. ALWAYS TRAIN WITH A PARTNER. This should help prevent a heavy barbell or dumbell falling on you whenever you perform limit or near-limit lifts. It's also a good idea if you are training at home to have someone nearby for the same reason. Safety apart, you'll find having a partner to encourage you is a great motivating influence; body building can be a solitary activity

2. ALWAYS USE COLLARS ON YOUR BARBELL. A common cause of injury in gyms and at home is where collars have been omitted from the end of a barbell during a heavy set. This can result in a plate falling off one end of the bar causing the other end to pivot bar upwards. The result? A potentially serious injury to yourself or your train-ing partner. Whilst it may seem time-consuming and inconvenient to replace these collars when you are chang-ing the weights', resultant injuries can often be far reaching, affecting your train-ing for many years to come.

3. ALWAYS KEEP THE GYM TIDY. Dumbells and bar-bells or loose plates lying on the gym floor are potentially extremely hazardous to your-self and other people train-ing. For this reason most gymnasiums supply racks for the equipment. This will mean that it's far easier for you to locate the equipment you require when you are training; it also reduces the risk of people tripping up on weights left around!

4. DON'T TRAIN IN AN OVER-CROWDED GYM. With the development and increasing popularity of the sport, many gymnasiums have become over-crowded. This means that you will often be forced to wait between sets, and since the body cools off rapidly, it's enough to cause injury. Far better to change your work-out hours to a much less crowded period.

5. WARM UP. In the same way as a cooled off body can suffer, it's also possible to injure yourself if you don't warm up correctly prior to a training session.

6. IMPROVE YOUR KNOW-LEDGE OF WEIGHT TRAIN-ING AND BODY BUILDING. One of the best ways to advance in the sport and to derive the maximum benefit from your training is to learn about it, both from publica-tions and other people in your gymnasium. If you're training at home you will have to rely on the many specialist magazines and books available from most good book shops. If training in a good gymnasium, the instructors should always be willing to impart tips and advice and give you all the assistance they can. Indeed, in many of the big gyms used by successful body building champions, you are also in a position to capitalise on their experience too.

Using a Gym

One of the most daunting things which confronts any newcomer in a gym is the vast array of equipment and machinery standing around.

Many gyms take each new member round all their equipment and explain how and when to use it. Even then it is often not possible to absorb everything in one session and it's amazing how busy the coach can be just when you have a question!

There are other gyms where no help is provided at all, but whatever the situation, most people only feel that they have arrived when they understand what everything is for. Until that time there's nothing more off-putting than smart alecks who rapidly move from one piece of equipment to another and who stand over you applying pressure just as you're trying to fathom how on earth something works. They may even establish their shortage of patience by 'tut tutting' or smiling superciliously, circumstances under which some new members crack.

They grab hold of a piece of equipment and misuse it completely rather than display their ignorance. This brings to the surface that even more infuriating smug expression which says it all: "This character doesn't know what on earth she's doing".

So to help familiarise you with your new gym, let's go through all the more familiar pieces of equipment, explaining how they work and what they are used for. The idea is not to make you an expert but to demystify the gym environment and allow you to ease your way around.

THE MULTIGYM

These are usually referred to as 8 station or 12 station gyms, which simply indicates roughly the umber of exercises that you can do on the machine. If you look around you will see that some gyms have charts on the wall near the multigym explaining how it works, but it's as well to have a head start.

THE LAT PULLDOWN MACHINE

As with nearly all the other stations this machine has a stack of weights with an adjustable pin. The higher the pin is located the lighter the stack will be. Most stacks are marked in pounds or kilos but until you get used to the exercise use the lightest weight. From then onwards use your discretion, increasing the level of difficulty as your progress allows.

Usually the pulldown machine has a long bar suspended overhead by a cable – and a seat placed underneath. Usually the bar is bent on either side to make it easy to grip, but sometimes it's straight. Don't be too concerned about the shape of the bar to start with.

Grasp the bar fairly wide, say with each hand a foot wider than shoulder width. Then whilst holding the bar sit down. Sometimes you will find a padded cross-piece under which you may place your knees. This helps to anchor you when you use heavier weights. With a steady movement pull the bar down behind your neck. Then allow it, under control, to go upwards; don't allow it to return to a rest position. The cable should be under tension at all times. As usual do 10 repetitions and get the feel of the machine. If it feels stiff rather than heavy, then it may need to be sprayed with some easing fluid. Ask the gym attendant to do this, if it proves necessary.

There are several variations to this exercise. One is where you lean back and pull the bar down to your chest, the other is where the bar is shorter and you bring it down to waist level.

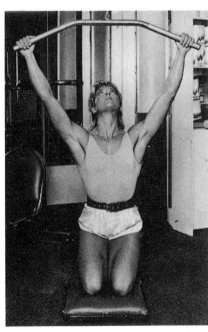

START   **FINISH**

This exercise and its variations work the lat muscles of the back. These are the muscles which start under the arm and taper into the waist. They make your back look athletic and with effort help create the illusion of a wasp-like waist.

TRICEPS PUSHDOWN MACHINE

This looks very similar to the lat pulldown station, except that the bar, which is considerably smaller, hangs much lower, usually round about chest height. Also the stack of weights are usually divided into much lighter units than the pulldown machine, and there will be no seating facility.

Grasp the bar with your hands 6in or less apart; your knuckles should face towards you, your palms away from you. Stand close to the bar and push it down until your arms straighten or 'lock out' at the elbow. Then slowly allow your arms to go upwards again, but no further than 45° above the horizontal position. Again the stack should not be allowed to return to a rest position and the whole exercise should be carried out under tension. Do 10 reps.

START

MIDPOINT

FINISH

This is one of the best exercises for the triceps, the muscles at the back of the arm, and is a must for all women who want to improve and build up their arms.

LAT ROWING MACHINE

Both stations up to now have operated in a vertical or up and down plane. The lat rowing machine, however, works in a horizontal plane, that is parallel to the floor.

Sometimes it's actually the same machine as the pull-down machine except that in this case you use a bar which is attached to a cable emerging near the floor. The bar is a

small one, about 1ft long. Alternatively there may be an attachment with two separate handles, one for each hand.

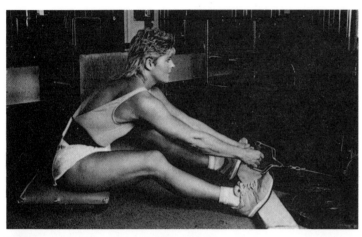

START

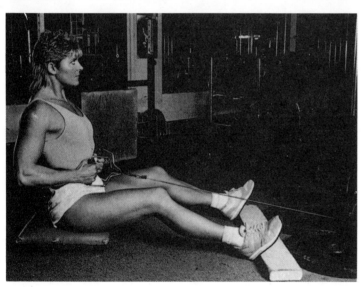

FINISH

In principle you sit on the floor with your feet positioned slightly apart, your knees bent with each foot placed on a pad. Whilst in the rest position you stretch forward towards the machine and at the same time grasp the bar or handles. Straighten your legs until your arms are stretched in front of you under tension. Then, without using your back, pull your arms towards you until the bar touches midway between your stomach and chest. Then under control allow your arm to return to a straight position whilst still under tension and so on. Do 10 repetitions.

This is a further key lat exercise.

HORIZONTAL LEG PRESS

This is another exercise which is done from the seated position. The seat on this occasion should have a very firm back support and be adjustable in the horizontal plane, that is backwards and forwards rather than up and down. When you sit in the seat you will see in front of you either one large pad on which to place both your feet or two smaller pads, one for each foot, depending on the design of the equipment. Put your feet on the pads and sit with your knees bent, tucking them up towards your chest. If your legs are fairly straight, then you need to adjust your seat forward until it's closer to the floor pad positions.

Perform this exercise by pushing your feet forward until your legs are straight and then SLOWLY allow them to return to their original position. If you allow the weights on the stack to come crashing down rather than under control, you will only be doing half the exercise, and ultimately you will also damage the machine. Note that on this machine the stack is on the far side of the multigym and not within reach whilst you

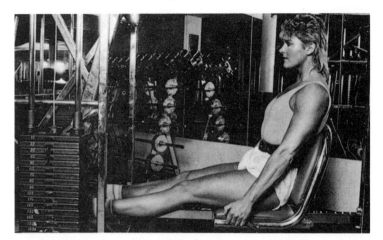

START

FINISH

are sitting on the machine. Again start off with a lighter weight until you get used to the movement. This won't take very long.

The exercise is for firming and building the quadraceps or quads, your powerful thigh muscles. As these are very strong don't wait for too many training sessions before increasing the weight and giving your legs a good testing workout. Incidentally the higher you place your feet on the pad or pads, the greater the degree of difficulty of the exercise.

Just a brief reminder of my own experience. When I first used this machine my legs increased in size fairly quickly and this alarmed me as I didn't want heavy legs. Never fear; all that is happening is that any fat which you may have, is being pushed outwards by the newly growing muscles. As your diet takes greater effect and that fat melts away, you will see your new shapely legs unveil themselves. If, however, your legs are a little bit too slim to start with then you'll be less concerned about this point.

There is another use for this machine and that is for training your calves. In this instance place the upper part of the soles of your feet very firmly on the pads with your heels overlapping at the bottom. Make absolutely sure that you have a good grip and that your feet won't slip. Push forward as before until your legs have straightened out. Now, keeping your legs in this position, push forward with your toes as far as you can. Hold for a count of two and then under strict control allow your toes to curl back as far as possible and then push forward with them again. Do 10 reps. At later workouts you can increase this to 15 and then 20 reps. As your calves are also very strong don't be afraid of increasing the weight. You may experience a burn in your calves. This is quite normal, but if you experience any sharp pain then stop immediately. This rule applies to all exercises though the calves are often the first place that new body builders experience a real burn.

Do the calf exercise with your toes pointed slightly inwards and if the design of the machine allows, also pointed slightly outwards. Make sure that your soles are planted extra firmly when doing the toes pointed outwards exercise to prevent your feet slipping off the pads. In each case do 10 reps and build up to an increased number of reps, adding weight as before.

▮ THE PRESS MACHINE

Here a bar is attached to the multigym at approximately shoulder level. The middle bit of the bar is scooped out so that you can grasp the end points in either hand at shoulder width, with your palms facing upwards and your knuckles facing behind you. Stand right underneath the bar. To do so you'll probably need to bend your knees. Start off by straightening your knees so that you are upright and the bar is under tension. Now press upwards until your arms are straight then lower slowly to your shoulders and repeat. Do 10 reps to start with. At later sessions steadily increase the weight with each of 3 sets.

This exercise is for your shoulders and is a basic building exercise. You'll probably notice that some people do this exercise with the bar behind their necks. This is a very effective variation of the exercise and one which you should try once you can do the basic movement I have just described.

BENCH PRESS MACHINE

This machine has a bar shaped similarly to that of the press machine except that it is probably attached to the multigym about mid-thigh level from the floor. You'll see a bench placed underneath the bar. After placing the pin at an appropriate point in the stack, lie on the bench face up with your head towards the stack and the bar across your chest. Grasp the bar wide so that your elbows are pointing away from your body on either side; the palms of your hands should face upwards with your knuckles pointing downwards. Now push upwards until your arms have straightened and then lower them under control; repeat. Do 10 reps. As you get used to the movement increase the weight steadily and aim for 3 × 10 reps.

START

FINISH

This is a chest or pecs exercise which will help support your bust. There's a variation with a narrow grip which will exercise your triceps more so than your pecs. However, it's usually better to exercise the triceps using free weights in an ordinary barbell; you can always use a narrower grip.

■ DIPPING BAR

Most multigyms have one of these machines attached somewhere. It's simply a U-shaped bar set parallel to the floor at about chest height, with handles for gripping at either end. Depending on how you use it, it can assist in working the chest or triceps.

In principle you grip the bar by the handles, hoist yourself in the air until your arms are locked out and your feet are off the ground. You then bend your legs at the knee and lower yourself by bending your arms at the elbows until your upper arms are

parallel to the floor, or even lower. Finish by pushing up until your arms are locked out again, then repeat the whole exercise. Normally this is done by more advance body builders, so only attempt it after your triceps have started to develop.

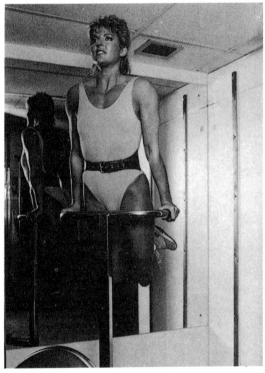

START

CHINNING BAR

This looks like a sloping lat pulldown bar, which has been attached solidly to the multigym about 8ft – 9ft off the ground. Again in principle, leap up and grasp the bar with a wide grip and then with your feet folded underneath, pull yourself up so that either your chest or the back of your neck is touching the bar. You then lower yourself making sure that your legs don't touch the floor, pull yourself up again and so on. The exercise is for building the lats and can also be performed with a narrow grip which is in fact easier. In all cases the exercise requires a considerable degree of strength to perform it properly, so only attempt it when you feel you're ready to move on to a much more advanced exercise.

START

FINISH

All of the multigym stations just described are manufactured as separate machines. These are likely to be found around the gym, and in each case they are used in exactly the same way as described for the multigym.

OTHER PIECES OF APPARATUS

Now let's look at some of the other pieces of equipment you will find in your gym.

BENCHES

Every gym has a range of benches complete with support stands. There are flat benches for all kinds of exercises, including pullovers, which were described earlier. Most common of all, however, is the bench press. You exercise on the bench press in exactly the same way as on the bench press machine attached to the multigym, except that here free weights are used on either side of a barbell. When doing this exercise always make sure that the weights are secured by collars and that someone is standing by when you pick up the barbell and replace it.

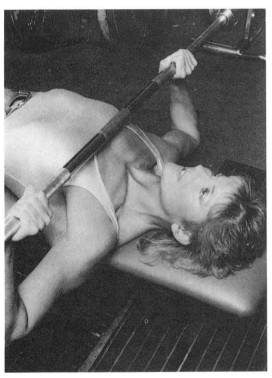

START

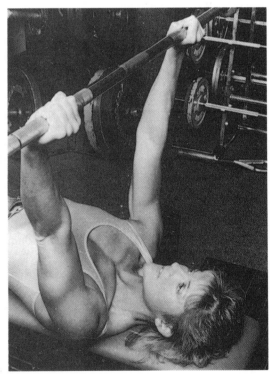

FINISH

There are several variations of the bench press. The exercise can be varied by using a narrow grip with your hands less than a shoulder's width apart. This works the triceps. Other exercises commonly carried out on the bench are dumbell presses. Perform both exercises in similar style to those you did at home, but note that the bench allows you a very much longer movement or stretch when lowering the dumbells.

BENCHES 2

You can also do leg raises on the bench. Whilst your body lies along the bench, allow your legs to overlap. This will allow you to stretch your abs a little more than when you are doing the exercise back at home.

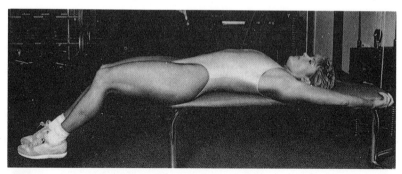

START

FINISH

Then there are a few variations of the bench itself. For example, there is the incline bench which is sometimes an adjustable version of the flat bench. It's used for pec exercises, such as incline bench presses, incline dumbell presses and incline flyes, which concentrate on a slightly higher part of the pectoral muscles. Usually the bench is not inclined much more than 45°. Once the bench is inclined much higher than this then the pressing movement works the shoulders. You will see people using dumbells and the barbell for presses. In principle this is a very disciplined way of doing the standing presses which you have been doing at home.

There is also the decline bench which doesn't seem to get used that often nowadays. Here you will see someone doing barbell or dumbell presses with their legs raised higher than their upper body. It's for the lowest part of pecs and seldom used by women.

PEC DECK

Whilst covering the chest training regimen, most gyms have the pec deck apparatus. You sit in the middle of this and then push your forearms together against the resistance as illustrated. This is a first class proven exercise for firming and developing the pectoral muscles.

START

FINISH

CABLE CROSS OVERS

Popular with more advanced body builders, this machine often occupies a prominent position in the gym. It involves standing between two stacks of weights and grasping two handles, one on either side. Your hands, palms facing down, begin at shoulder level in a crucifix position and finish more or less in front of the groin. It's for bringing up striations in the pecs, and not a machine to use until you are really much more advanced.

START

FINISH

There are a whole host of machines and equipment devoted to your legs.

SQUAT RACK

This assists you in doing your squats. It allows you to load the barbell and place it on your shoulders with the minimum of difficulty, before squatting in exactly the same way you have been doing at home.

START

FINISH

LEG EXTENSION – LEG CURL MACHINE

No gym is without one. However, different machines will vary in their effectiveness as well as the smoothness with which they respond to your efforts.

Do the leg extensions whilst sitting upright on the padded surface of the machine with your legs bent at the knee and the lower of the machine's two pads across your shins. You then straighten your legs, using the large quadricep muscles of the front of the thigh until your legs are straight and parallel to the floor. Count up to two and then lower your legs under strict control. Make sure that your bottom stays down and concentrate on using your legs and not swaying your body.

START

FINISH

Leg curls exercise the back of the legs or leg biceps and the glutes or bottom. Lay face down on the machine with your calves (just above the Achilles' tendon) pushing against the upper of the machine's two pads. Then bend your knees as far as you can, usually until the pad touches your bottom. Hold for a count of two and then let your legs return to a straight position. At all costs try to keep your bottom from jutting upwards by pressing your hips against the machine's padded surface.

■■ INCLINE OR VERTICAL LEG PRESS ■■

This is similar to the horizontal leg press machine on the multigym. The only difference is that you lie with the back support underneath you rather than being an up-right position. You'll also be pushing the weight upwards which is more difficult than moving it backwards and forwards. Usually the machine has a built-in safety device which you control with your hands. Make sure that this has been properly demonstrated before you attempt to use the machine.

START

HACK SQUAT MACHINE

This is a tough one for which you need some early supervision. You fit into the machine by leaning backwards against its padded surface with your feet flat against an inclined surface. Usually there are two pads, one on either side of your head, resting on your shoulders. You then release the machine's safety device to take the weight on your shoulders and squat in the same plane in which the machine moves. A deep squat is important. You then use the quads (thigh muscles) and particularly those round your knees to straighten up and so on. Whatever you do make sure that you start this exercise with very light weights, say 10lbs maximum and that a 'spotter' – or helper is standing by.

START **FINISH**

CALF MACHINE

This works on a similar principle to the calf work which you have been doing at home. The only difference is that it adds weight which you have to support on your shoulders.

Adjust the machine so that the pads rest on your shoulders whilst placing the balls of your feet on the foot rest. Your heels should be overlapping and your knees bent. Then straighten your knees until you are standing upright. Wear a belt to minimise lower back strain. Now do your calf raises in the usual way. Do sets of 20 with your toes pointing straight ahead, pointing inwards and pointing outwards. Your calves are strong and you should soon be able to increase the weight you are using over the machine's stack.

TOP POSITION

LOWER POSITION

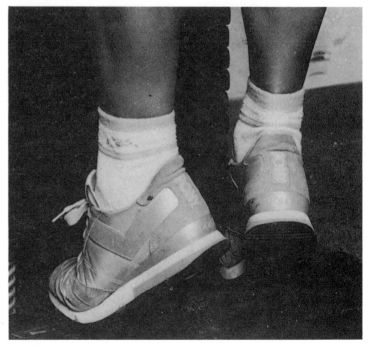

TOES POINTING OUTWARDS

■ PREACHER BENCH

These are pieces of apparatus, like the bench, rather than machines.

The preacher bench allows you to do biceps exercises very strictly. Sit upright on the backless seat and lean forwards with the back of your arms resting on the padded preacher surface. You need a spotter to hand you a barbell. Usually I prefer a straight bar to an EZ bar, so called because it's bent like a Z. Take the bar in the lower position, with your arms straight, and then curl it upwards to your chin. Again this is a more advanced exercise.

FINISH

HYPEREXTENSION CHAIR

The hyperextension chair is specifically for the hyper-extensions exercise. It varies a lot in design but in principle the chair is raised off the floor to at least waist level and you always need to manoeuvre yourself into it. Lie face down on a pad which supports your hips and upper thigh whilst your calves fit under another pad. Your trunk is free to fall forwards and hyper-extend upwards. Do the exercise as before only over a longer range. It's a toughie!

START

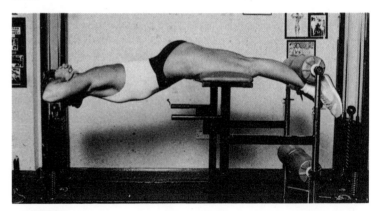

MIDPOINT

FINISH

ABDOMINAL BOARDS

Lastly there are abdominal boards which are used for sit-ups. Rather than a heavy piece of furniture, the board has a pad for you to put your feet under. Another variation is that the boards slot into a rack on the wall so that they rest at an angle, but there's no need to incline the boards at more than 45°. Obviously the steeper the incline the harder the exercise becomes. Otherwise do your sit-ups in the normal way.

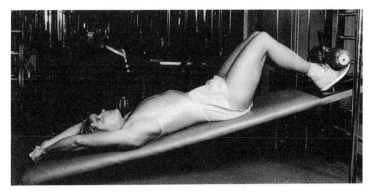

START

FINISH

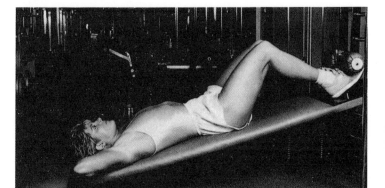

START (ADVANCED)

FINISH (ADVANCED)

■ SOME ADDITIONAL GYM EXERCISES ■

There are two free weight exercises which should form part of a gym programme but which up to now have not been included in your planned home schedules.

■ BARBELL CURL ■

This is very similar to dumbell curls except that you use a barbell for the exercise. There are two variations which affect different areas of the bicep. In the first of these hold your hands close together, say about 3in – 4in apart; the other involves a wider grip, in which case place your hands just 2in – 3in wider than shoulder level in each case. As I mentioned earlier I prefer a straight bar to an EZ bar because from the body building point of view although the EZ bar is easier to grip, the straight bar helps you to get more of a peak on the biceps.

■ UPRIGHT ROWS ■

This is a good exercise for the traps and shoulders. It's also fairly useful as a stamina builder when you keep your rest periods between sets at a minimum.

Grasp the bar with your hands about 6in apart with the back of your hands facing away from you. Stand upright with your shoulders straight and your arms stretched down in front of your thighs. Pull the barbell up to your chin and try and hold it there for a split second to start with, or if possible a count of two. Then lower it under control and repeat. It's not easy but it's good. Try it with a light barbell, say 25lbs to start.

START

FINISH

BEGINNER'S PROGRAMME
(Three times per week)

Body Part	Exercise	Sets	Reps
CHEST	Flat bench press	3 × 10	
	OR		
	Incline dumbell press	3 × 10	
	Flat flyes	3 × 10	
BACK	Wide grip behind		
	Lat pull	3 × 10	
	Long pulley rows	3 × 10	
SHOULDERS	Multigym press in front of neck	3 × 10	
	(Upright rowing	3 × 10	
	OR		
	Lateral raises)	3 × 10	
ARMS	Standing barbell curls	3 × 10	
	Seated dumbell curls	3 × 10	
	Close grip bench press	3 × 10	
	Triceps pushdown	3 × 10	
ABS	Sit-ups	3 × 10	
	Leg raises	3 × 10	
LEGS	Leg press (multigym)	3 × 10	
	Leg extensions	3 × 10	
	Leg curls	3 × 10	
	Standing calf raises	3 × 10	

Diet and Nutrition

Wherever in the world body builders gather you can bet that after a very short while the conversation inevitably focuses on those subjects surrounded by so much mystery and myth, dieting and nutrition. Almost every competitor has some tale to tell and of late, at contest time and at some of the seminars that I have given, I have heard quite a few.

THE DANGERS OF A BAD DIET

It's astonishing how many people still use a low carbohydrate diet to get into shape. There's no doubt that in some cases it will get a competitor 'cut up', but at what cost?

When body builders go on a contest diet they all have the same goal; to lose all visible body fat and excess fluid, without sacrificing any muscle size. A pretty difficult feat. To understand what makes it difficult, let's look at what happens if we diet without training at all.

First we lose weight and fat in particular, but then as Geoffrey Cannon in his book "Dieting Makes You Fat" explains, the body begins to get worried. It begins to believe that there is a famine coming and so it adapts to the new situation.

What happens is our metabolism slows down as a protective measure. It does so to ensure we conserve energy. The body tries to stick to the composition that it has at the time. It needs to keep fat as well as muscle stored for that famine. This means we lose weight very slowly.

Sometimes people on a diet get very worried at this point and they lower the amount of calories they are eating even further. The body panics, the metabolism slows down even more and so on.

There are many women whose lives consist of blowing up after months of careless eating, followed by dieting, say to get into a bikini for the summer holiday. They follow this by blowing up, followed by dieting and so it goes on. Each time it seems as if their tough disciplined diet is returning them to their former slim condition, but sadly this is not so, for each time they are retaining a higher and higher proportion of body fat.

This is precisely because of the process which I have just described. The first time dieting down takes place the body hangs on to a higher proportion of fat than expected because it believes there is a famine on the way. As a result, the 'slim', say 119lbs (8st 7lbs) is lighter in weight but not quite as toned due to a higher proportion of fat to lean muscle tissue.

Therefore when the cycle continues and a new binge ensues, the person concerned will yet again have a higher proportion of fat.

Each time round, the 119lb target is reached through strict dieting alone, the body hangs on to even more fat. Therefore each time the physique is less toned and even at 119lbs looks worse and worse as it speedily becomes 'fatter'. Year by year the body holds on to ever higher proportions of fat compared to lean muscle tissue. And as I have said before, and will say again, because it's so important, you can't tone fat.

Body builders counter this whole process by training and stimulating their muscles and forcing them to grow. Usually they take in enough protein to ensure that the muscle is fed and that the growth continues, but we need energy to train.

So where is that energy going to come from? If the number of carbohydrates or calories we eat are too low, the body has a problem.

It's got to get its energy from somewhere and what is it that body builders have got in abundance? Why, muscles of course. The body burns off some of the muscle tissue to provide energy and so all that hard work goes down the drain. The body also tends to slow down the metabolism as well, which is why some of us find that last little bit of fat so hard to lose.

One variation of the contest diet is the low carbohydrate diet. In theory we can eat plenty of protein so we shouldn't go hungry and the muscles are being fed all the time; the body burns off all the excess which we carry to provide us with the energy to train. There is an instant effect. In the first week anything up to 10lbs can be lost and this is a terrific encouragement. But what is actually happening is that all we are losing is fluid.

Carbohydrate helps us hold fluid in a proportion of roughly one gram of carbohydrate to three grams of fluid. No carbs being consumed means a lot of fluid just drops off, but from that point on the metabolism slows down with a vengeance. Very soon there's little energy left to train with because carbohydrate is the prime source of that energy.

But there is worse to follow: we become irrational and very irritable, because the body has no immediate source of sugars, which it takes from carbohydrates, and the brain needs sugar to function properly. Muscle tissue gets converted to sugar but this is not an efficient method and so we remain tired, bad tempered, edgy and irrational.

I remember many years ago sharing a table at a post-contest dinner with Terry Phillips, who was eating his last normal meal before beginning his long contest diet. It was his wife who paled and looked apprehensive. I soon learned why. I remember how difficult and irrational I used to become in those days when I used a low carbohydrate diet.

The other unfortunate side effect of being on a low carb diet, which may make us loony, is that very lack of mental control. You may begin to crave for certain forms of carbohydrate, usually concentrated carbs such as ice-cream or chocolate. Every now and again the craving becomes so strong that it becomes impossible not to take just a mouthful to relieve the obsession. But because we do not have a strong control over our minds, that one spoonful can often lead to an uncontrolled binge.

One experienced body builder told of a recent occasion where this happened to him to such a degree that he had to abandon months of plans to compete. Another top class competitor related how just a little taste of ice-cream resulted in his consuming more than a litre in one go! He just lost control. It's a very familiar story.

There is only one way round all this which is to lose weight slowly. You should do this by reducing the number of calories you are consuming by a small but meaningful amount over a period of several months. At the same time you should increase your aerobic activity to ensure that the metabolism speeds up. This will assist with the process of burning fat rather than encouraging the body to adapt to famine.

There is another process which concerns body builders, which we call 'carbing up'. This involves taking in more carbohydrate then usual a day or two before a contest to fill the muscles with glycogen and make them look fuller. The principle that allows this to happen is that any excess won't show up for three days or more. Sounds simple yet an awful lot can go wrong; but this shouldn't concern you for a while yet.

As you can see I have been concerned about diet and nutrition for quite some time, so let's look at some of the pointers which can help you.

A BALANCED DIET

Food is a stimulus to the body and we respond to each kind of food differently. There is also a different kind of biochemical reaction in each case too; some responses are quick (starch, carbohydrates for energy) some are fairly slow acting (vitamin A, proteins) but for complete well being, we need a little of everything to play a part in our training.

Here are some of the basic definitions which will help you make sure that your diet has an adequate balance of necessary nutrients.

CALORIES

These are not a food of course: they are the means of measuring how much energy is being burned up by the body, in other words, units of energy. One calorie is the amount of heat necessary to raise the temperature of one gram of water by 1°.

PROTEINS

Essentially these are a compound of carbon hydrogen and oxygen and nitrogen. They are essential for all living structures and for every cell in your body. Their main function is to provide for growth and repair, but any excess can be converted into glucose and then used to provide energy. As they are made up of amino acids, which cannot be made by the body itself, they must be taken into the body as food.

As I have already explained, one of the problems with low carbohydrate diets is that when we lack carbs the body converts protein into energy. This takes it away from its natural function of body building.

Although many of the new nutritionists believe that Western diets for an ordinary sedentary life are unnecessarily high in protein, it's important for a body builder in training to have enough extra protein for conversion into the required muscle growth.

It's also important to have the right kind of protein. Foods from animal sources (milk, eggs, fish, meat) provide first class protein and have more essential amino acids than vegetable sources. This means that vegetarian body builders will have to ensure that they eat a reasonable quantity of at least milk and eggs with their vegetarian diet, or their diet will be quite inadequate.

High quality protein
Poultry
Fish
Meat
Milk products including yoghurt, cheese
Eggs

FATS

The most concentrated form of energy, a gram of fat, has double the calories of a gram of protein or carbohydrate. It is satisfying, filling, and long-lasting, and animals store it for energy. BUT we actually need far less fat than we consume, and reducing fat intake is the easiest way of cutting down on calories in a controlled diet.

There are two kinds of fat, unsaturated and saturated.

Saturated fats are found in solid animal fats such as lard, non-skimmed and non fat-reduced milk products, egg yolks and coconut. They are thought to have a consider-ably harmful effect on the body, adding to heart disease, blood problems and a host of other modern illnesses. Unsaturated fats are probably the safest for the serious body builder to consume; you'll find them primarily in fish, vegetable seed grain and nut oils.

Be warned: some products that are advertised as low fat are still quite high in calories. Low fat spreads may contain half as many calories as butter but that's still an awful lot of calories!

Recommended sources of fat
Fish and fish oils
Sunflower, sassflower, corn oils
Nut oils

To avoid: butter and margarines, hard cheese, fatty meat, lards and suets, avocado oils and whole milk

CARBOHYDRATES

Carbohydrates are made up of three main groups, sugars, starches and celluloses. Sugars and starches are the body's preferred source of energy, and occur naturally in fruits and vegetables. Most of our carbohydrates used to come from starches – potatoes, breads, grains. Today our consumption of sugars has risen dramatically, and it seems clear that a good body building diet should aim to revert to a higher pro-portion of starch, especially from wholemeal flours, whole grains, and so on. Not enough is really known about the differences between sugars and starches for general health, but most doctors now agree that a low carbohydrate diet is not good for long-term nutrition.

The recommended balance of the latest nutritional research is that we include 60% natural carbohydrate in our diet, 15% fat and only 25% protein. If anything, this should vary by increasing carbohydrate rather than fat.

■ COMPLETE CARBOHYDRATES (STARCHES) ■

When plants form sugars by the action of sunlight (photosynthesis), they store them in their stems, roots or seeds as starch. Starch is the main source of energy for plants; it also provides us with our best system of energy without the problems we associate with refined sugar.

Recommended high sources of complex carbohydrates (starches)

Wholegrain cereals and flours (and any breads, cakes etc. made with them)
Grains such as brown or natural rice
Potatoes
Beans, pulses (lentils etc.), sweetcorn

Some fruits such as bananas (Other vegetables also contain some carbohydrates, but in lesser amounts).

An important point which is special to the requirements of body building: in spite of all the persuasive advertisements and commercials, don't train on an apple; its simple sugars will be used up too quickly. A banana is better, but best of all, believe it or not, is a baked potato!

■ SIMPLE CARBOHYDRATES (SUGARS) ■

Basically these have no other use in the body except as a source of quick energy. When the body takes in too much sugar, more natural insulin is produced than can be cleared from the system, and in response the blood sugar level drops too far! This leads almost immediately to a feeling of fatigue, tiredness and irritability. So it's important to stabilise the level of sugar in the body at the right amount. We should really never need to add any refined or artificial sugars to our diet because sugar occurs naturally in fruits, some vegetables and in honey. Refined sugar is now regarded as being extremely dangerous, causing not only obesity but also contributing to the problems of heart disease, liver disease, tooth decay and gum problems, and so on.

High source of sugar
Refined sugar

Recommended sources of sugar
Natural sugars in fruit (fructose)
Honey
Vegetables, particularly when young (carrots and peas especially)
Naturally dried fruits (with no added sugar)
LXC
Lactose in milk
Glucose

To avoid: refined sugars (sucrose) as in sugar syrups, processed foods, jams, cakes, biscuits etc.

FIBRES

This is an indigestible form of carbohydrate which used to be known of as roughage. It's essential for the efficient working of your digestion and the elimination of waste products through the bowel system, and people who eat a high level of fibre in their diet are far less likely to suffer from diseases of any part of the digestive tract. Most fruit and vegetables contain some fibre but it's not always easy to assess exactly how much.

RECOMMENDED SOURCES OF FIBRE

The easiest way to ensure a good source of fibre in a diet is to eat plenty of fruit and vegetables, and to add wheat or soya bran to your food every day. A few teaspoonfuls are usually enough.

Soluble fibre
Pectin from apples
Porridge oats

Insoluble fibre
Bran
Vegetables (spinach and broccoli in particular)

EATING FOR TRAINING

The body can only assimilate a relatively small amount of protein at a time. So if your main aim is to add more muscle, then it's a good plan to change your habits to include five or six small meals a day instead of one big one and two smaller ones.

If you want to gain weight, or are putting on a lot of muscle, then you might want to add a protein powder based on egg and skimmed milk to your diet. These are available in powdered form, and you can mix a tablespoon into your morning porridge, or you can make up a protein drink as directed, with skimmed milk, instead of coffee or tea. You can do the same mid-afternoon, and last thing at night. It's also a good idea to pace your additional supplements by adding only one a day until you are certain you are not simply putting on weight and that you are training enough to make sure that the weight is muscle and not fat!

There are also some general guidelines to follow. You will need to vary your main meals, of course, so try to have liver once a week and restrict your egg dishes to three a week. Cottage cheese is one of the most adaptable foods on the market, and it can be mixed with almost anything, even hot or cold dishes, as well as salads.

If you are training really actively, then you can increase the number of egg dishes per week because your body will burn up the extra cholesterol, but if you're using these notes as strict maintenance guidelines, then stick to having eggs no more than three times a week. If training and you want to lose weight as well, follow the general guidelines but cut out additional fat completely (1lb of fat is 3,500 calories) as all your meats will contain enough fat for maintenance. Don't cut out any of the 'types' of food, cut down instead on the amounts you eat. Restrict your fruit to two pieces a day, and learn gradually to do without desserts, which except for fruit, are empty calories with nothing but refined sugar to be gained.

The best way to lose weight is by a combination of reduced calories and increased exercise: the 'plus and minus' diet. You can get protein from grilled chicken or white turkey meat, without the skin; fish should be of the low-calorie varieties like cod or haddock and grilled without butter. Use plenty of herbs and spices and lots of lemon juice, but no salt. Cut out red meat and liver. Try making a salad dressing with lemon juice. Look for tinned fish in brine rather than oil – tuna and sardines are both available now canned in brine. If you can't find fresh fruit, most supermarkets stock fruit canned without syrup. Read all labels carefully.

Remember also that yoghourt and skimmed milk still have a lot of calories, so change your drinking habits. Try to have your coffee black.

Stick to low calorie fruits like strawberries (the lowest of all), blackberries, raspberries, green apples, melon, gooseberries and so on. Keep away from avocados – over 300 calories in just one half! Avoid all dried fruits while you are training to lose weight and remember that grapes and bananas are pretty high in calories. When you reach your ideal weight, then maintain it by sensible regular eating.

■CAROLYN'S DIET ■

The diet that follows is typical of one I might use. It's for one day only, but it should give you an idea of the type of eating I not only advocate, but practice on a regular basis, whether training intensively or not.

Breakfast
Piece of fresh fruit (an orange, grapefruit or an apple)
One bowl of porridge made with water or skimmed milk (sweeten if necessary with a few raisins or sultanas or a spoonful of honey)
I eat breast fillets of chicken for breakfast, but most people might prefer eggs, poached, boiled or scrambled without butter
Wholemeal toast
Yoghourt (natural, unsweetened)
Black coffee or tea (no sugar)

Mid-morning break
Piece of fruit
Slice of crispbread with cottage cheese
Yoghourt or skimmed milk
Wholemeal roll

Lunch
Grilled chicken or turkey breast
or
Jacket baked potato
Piece of fresh fruit or fresh fruit salad
Yoghourt

Mid-afternoon break
Wholemeal high bran roll, with cottage cheese

Dinner
Grilled fish
or
Lean meat
or
Liver
Salad, including tomato and carrot, or fresh vegetables
Baked compote of fruit
(If at the end of the day you are still hungry, have a glass of skimmed milk before going to bed)

Combine diet with training for a good physique

SUPPLEMENTS OR NOT?

Unless you are able to ensure that you have only organically grown and unprocessed food, it is almost impossible to know how much of the vitamin and mineral content has been lost. So I believe in taking supplements. I think general multi-vitamin and minerals tablets in the recommended dose are always important for women and body builders.

Zinc: This helps to repair tissue, promote growth and is particularly useful in extra quantities when you have a strain or sprained muscle. There also seems to be a possible link between *anorexia nervosa* and zinc deficiency, a view which is reinforced by the fact that many women have low levels of zinc in their bodies. The other supplements I would recommend are as follows, but there are, of course, many others as you see from the next page.

Calcium: Calcium is important if you are on a low calorie diet (often low in calcium). It's also good if pregnant, to maintain bones and good teeth. Take the recommended dose of usually one tablet a day.

Vitamin C: It's difficult to judge how much vitamin C there is in an orange because we don't know how long it has been stored or how it has been treated. So even though you think you are eating enough citrus and other fresh fruit, it's a good idea to take extra vitamin C. I'm a great believer in it and take at least 4000mg a day, but this is not necessarily advisable unless you are in training and working very hard.

Vitamin B6: This helps the body assimilate protein and is useful in preventing premenstrual tension. If you also suffer from fluid retention just before your period, then an extra dose of B6 will help.

Vitamin D: In winter it may be helpful to have a little extra vitamin D, but do be careful. It is stored in the body as well as being fat soluble, so only follow the recommended dosage given on the bottle.

VITAMIN AND MINERAL CHECK

The charts that follow are a basic guideline for good nutrition. I show the average adult requirements. Pregnant and breast-feeding women should take the highest amounts, plus a little extra. Check with your doctor if in doubt, or you think you have particular needs; we are all different after all.

MINERALS	RECOMMENDED AMOUNT	
SODIUM –SODIUM CHLORIDE (table salt)	Basic eating with no salt added will still give you five times the amount you need, which is about $^1/_5$ of a teaspoonful a day.	
CALCIUM	Teenagers and pregnant women Adults	1,200mg 80mg
IRON	Teenagers and pregnant women Adult males Women	80mg 10mg 18mg
MAGNESIUM	Teenagers Adults Pregnant women	350mg–400mg 300mg 450mg
IODINE	Males – 130 mcg to 100 as older Females – 115 mcg to 80 as older	
PHOSPHORUS	As above	
ZINC	Teenagers and adults Pregnant women	15mg 20mg

NUTRIENT	R.D.A.	FOODS RICH IN
VITAMIN K (Folic Acid)	400mg	Legumes, vegetables, fruits, juices
NIACIN (Nicotinic Acid)	13mg	Soybeans, greens, beans and grains
RIBOFLAVIN B2	1.2mg	Milk, leafy green vegetables, beans
THIAMIN B1	1.0mg	Yeasts, whole grains, legumes
B6 PYRIDOXINE	2.0mg	Whole grains, beans, some vegetables (but destroyed by heat and processing)
B12	3.0mg	Milk and most milk products, except for butter
VITAMIN A	800-4000 IU	Dark green leafy vegetables, deep orange vegetables, in fruits, some meats, milk, eggs
VITAMIN D	400 IU	Dairy products, milk, some in egg yolks, butter
VITAMIN E	9–15 IU	Oils, nuts, grains, some vegetables, fruits, chocolate; but not in large quantities, so you'd need a lot of bulk Grains contribute, but need a lot of bulk to be sole supply Vegetables are a little better Fruits poor (except for wild blackberries)
VITAMIN C	45mg	Fresh fruit and vegetables (is stable in citrus fruits, but may be lost easily in storage and cooking)

NOTE: Recommended amounts are generally higher than absolute minimum required.

Body Building as a Competitive Sport

Body building may seem like a sport concerned primarily with your own personal development, but nowadays, it's very much more. Under the auspices of the International Federation of Body Builders (IFBB) your new hobby has the support of 127 nations. That makes the IFBB the world's sixth largest sports federation.

A whole host of opportunities are afforded our top amateur women. There are the annual European and World Championships and, once every four years, the World Games, besides a large number of local, area and national championships. Those of you who wish to take your training further and compete, reap the benefit of the IFBB's and its affiliate the EFBB's efforts over the past five years.

But it wasn't always like that, and it has largely been through the productivity of IFBB President, Ben Weider, and the encouragement of his brother, Joe Weider, that women's body building has now gained wide acceptance. Nowadays it's commonplace to see models posing with dumbells or showing some muscle in most popular womens' magazines, and it was in Joe Weider's *MUSCLE AND FITNESS* that body build-

ers were first featured. By showcasing women in this way, including a large number of super cover shots, Joe started the ball rolling. He then took matters further by adapting his well-known body building principles to meet the requirements of female enthusiasts. With *SHAPE* magazine designed specifically for women and, the new lifestyle *MUSCLE AND FITNESS*, Joe continues to support the interest of women at every level. His contribution to body building in general is immeasurable.

When I started to compete in the physical culture contest era which preceded body building, I was often horrified by the attitude of judges. One, who chain smoked

throughout, stands out particularly in my mind. Fortunately times have changed, and when you compete in an EFBB contest things are very different.

All of our judges have to attend a special seminar where procedures are outlined, the conduct expected of our judges clarified and a short test undertaken. After this the judges have to do a number of test papers at local or qualifying contests to prove their competence, before finally being accepted as regular qualified judges. This all helps to ensure competence and fairness towards our competitors, who after all make enormous sacrifices and are more than entitled to a fair deal.

Julian often acts as a judge

The Competition Poses

To the right you can see the five main poses used in competition. They are designed to show all the muscles in every part of the body to best advantage.

Front double biceps

Side Chest

Back and double biceps

Triceps

Abs and thighs

Julie's big day!

JULIE'S BIG DAY

It's just possible that you are becoming really excited about the progress you are making. Are you beginning to look in the mirror and think "I look just as good as those body builders, in fact better than most of them. I bet I could win one of those contests!"?

But what would you be letting yourself in for?

Body building is a little different from most sports activities. As a netball, tennis or softball enthusiast about to play in your very first competitive match, the chances are that you would appear before a few friends and relatives on some obscure court or field. With body building, almost certainly you will make your debut before several hundred, or maybe even a thousand, fee-paying spectators. It can be daunting and does require a little bit of bottle, but this is what makes body builders a bit special!

The one consolation to all this is that you are unlikely to be the lone debutante. Body building has become so popular that there are always one or two newcomers trying their luck at every contest.

So that you might know what such a debut is like, I asked Julie McDonald, a welcome new face amongst British body builders, to reconstruct what a first contest experience

is all about. With the help of Rena Pearl's photographs, we capture her day at the London Championships. Accompanied by her husband Adrian, let's follow Julie's progress through her own imagined words, thoughts and feelings.

The butterflies begin as soon as the venue is in sight. But if you have prepared properly it's a good feeling. You're about to put yourself to the test. Julie and Adrian have

travelled a long way, from Crewe, when they spy the formidable Hammersmith Town Hall Building. It's a big hall but there seem to be few spectators milling about outside and in the entrance.

"Doesn't seem to be much happening," says Julie. "Are you sure we're at the right place?"
"No doubt about it," replies Adrian, "but we're a bit late."
"Gosh, I hope I haven't missed the weigh in, not after

Hope we haven't missed the weigh in

training so hard and travelling so far."

Most body building contests specify that entries must be received about a week beforehand, though some require just two or three days notice. On arrival at the hall the first thing that competitors have to do is register, which tells the organisers that they have arrived. Soon afterwards the competitor weighs in. There are two classes: up to 52kg, that is 114lbs or 8st 2lbs (lightweight) and over 52kg (middleweight). Contestants have to specify in which class they are competing and then make the weight on the day. Sometimes a competitor may be just over the limit. This is a disadvantage in that if they compete as a middleweight they would be the tiniest in their class. They could, if they wished, be allowed a half hour to take off the excess and then be re-weighed.

Sometimes it works the other way and a contestant who is just under the limit may decide that the lightweights have several outstanding entries and that it would be easier to win the middleweight class. In this case they would have half an hour to put on any extra weight to go up a class.

Winning is important because this is an English Federation of Body Builders (EFBB) qualifying event. The winners go through to the British Finals and the winners there get sent all over the world to the European and the World Championships and even the World Games.

Look, there's Golds' stall

Julie is just on the lightweight limit so she wants to be sure of where she will be competing. They enter the hall. In the foyer they see an array of stalls selling gym clothing, food supplements, photographs, books and magazines.

"Look," exclaims Julie. "There's the Gold's stall with all those super things that we can never get at home. I must buy one of those track suits right away!"

Julie McDonald, lightweight, No. 7

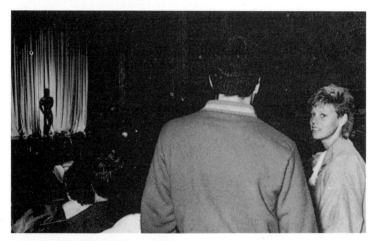

Look, they're already judging the juniors

Look at him!

"Hmm! I think you'd better register and weigh in first," cautions Adrian.

Julie has her name checked on the competitors list by an official and is the directed to the 'weigh in'. This is held either back stage or in one of the warm-up or changing areas.

"Thank goodness, there are still one or two waiting to weigh in so I won't be last", says Julie. "I'll just have a little trial with all my clothes on." The rules are that the weigh in should be carried out whilst wearing a competitor's costume, but the kindly official looks down and seeing that Julie is under the limit announces, "Julie Mac-Donald, lightweight, number seven." He hands Julie a cardboard number with safety pins attached which later she'll pin to her costume.

"Women's lighweights will be judged after the men's lightweights. Before that there are the men's junior, men's novices and the over 40's, so you have a couple of hours to spare," says the official. "Don't go too far away and listen for the call for the women competitors."

Most contests are pre-judged during the day, with the finals in the evening. There are two rounds of judging. In the first the judges look at all the qualities of the physiques: they look for muscle size, definition, shape and balance. Competitors walk out on to the stage in a line and face the judges, who make an overall assessment. They then do four quarter turns, always to the right so that the judges can see them from every angle. After this they leave the stage and return individually to do five compulsory poses, the 'double biceps', 'side chest', 'back double biceps' 'showing the calf', 'triceps' and 'abdominals and thigh'. All the while the judges make their notes.

All competitors are then recalled on stage and the judges make comparisons. A maximum of three contestants are called forward simultaneously and taken through the compulsory poses. This allows the judges to assess them really closely. The judges can call for as many sets of comparisons as they wish until they are completely satisfied, at which point all the competitors leave the stage for a second time. The judges then place the competitors from first to last, on their official score sheets, with low scores indicating the highest position. The winner gets a score of one, the second competitor, a two and so on. These scores are then handed in to the statistician. If a judge is way out of line with the others or shows a blatant bias toward a particular competitor, then the statistician brings this to the attention of the head judge. This official doesn't score the contest but is responsible for the conduct

And there's Carolyn and Ken Latham

Oiling up

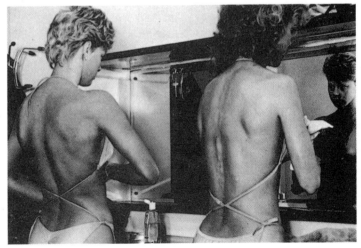

It's nearly time . . .

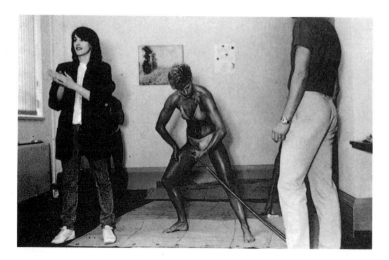

Here's Maxcine Mason

the audience. When they have all finished, the top three finalists (occasionally it may be more) are called back on to the stage for the pose-down. This is the last round of judging in which the finalists do the compulsory poses simultaneously under the guidance of the head judge; they then pose against each other without restriction for about a minute. Audiences find this very exciting and it gives the judges one last opportunity to make their assessments. Their scores as before are added to their previous totals and the results calculated. Then the winners and top places are announced and the trophies and medals presented.

But back to Julie and Adrian who have made their way into the hall.

"They're already judging the juniors," observes Julie. "Look how full the hall is and this is only the judging! The lighting looks good too."

"Yes," agrees Adrian, "and lighting is so important. If too flat, like that from a spot light, then all your muscles appear smooth and the spectators and judges can't see your physique. But here there's plenty of overhead light angled down to give just enough contrast to show all the definition. Let's go and check if there are any seats near the front where we can see better."

of the judges and the competitors. In the case of biased scoring he or she warns the offending judges and under some circumstances will even cancel their scores.

Once the head judge is satisfied, the competitors are called on stage one at a time for the second round of the contest. This involves posing to music for one and a half minutes. The judges make their assessments and again score the competitors from

first to last. They are still looking at the physique, but this time competitors have a chance to show themselves without being restricted to the compulsory poses. Naturally some credit is given for the style in which they display their physiques. The first and second round scores are added together and this completes the pre-judging.

In the evening competitors repeat their posing, but this time it's just for the benefit of

"What about those two seats behind the judges. Seeing that you are a competitor we might be able to sit there. Look at that junior. He's tremendous," says Adrian. "Golly, that's Carolyn, and there's Ken Latham, the EFBB Treasurer who's judging. I'd better keep quiet, I don't want to upset his concentration."

All too soon there's the call for the lightweight women to get ready and Julie has to go to the changing room. She gets into her bikini, and checks everything in the mirror, whilst she rubs on some coconut oil. Mineral oil and baby oil are too shiny and not permitted. Julie looks anxious as she realises her moment will soon be due.

"Okay, Julie, time to pump up," advises Adrian, taking out a set of expanding springs. They move to the warm-up room. Adrian puts his foot on one of the springs and Julie grasps the other and does some concentration curls.

Julie looks up and sees Maxcine Mason arrive. She's tough to beat, Julie concludes. Maxcine was runner-up at the British Championships last time and is on the championship trail again. Gosh look at those abs. Now Maxcine's doing a lat spread.

"I don't have to do that Adrian, do I?" Julie asks

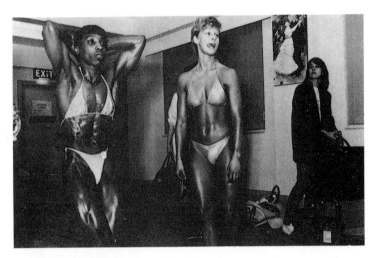

Maxcine flexing her abs

Do I have to do a lat spread too?

anxiously. Adrian shakes his head reassuringly.

Then it's up the stairs and on to the stage. Julie stands in the line and does her quarter turns with all the others. They go on one at a time to do their compulsory poses. Julie's worried that she'll make mistakes and forget what to do. But there's no need for any anxiety because the head judge announces each pose and guides her whenever she goes astray.

They all troop back on and the comparisons begin. At first they don't call Julie at all. It's mainly the top national competitors, Maxcine Mason and Diana Defries, and impressive new star Frankie Hutchinson, who are being looked at.

"Please remember me," thinks Julie. Suddenly she hears number seven called, and Julie walks forward with Frankie Hutchinson and Diana Defries.

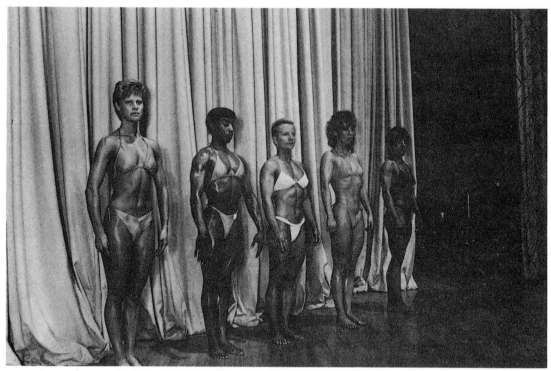

Julie's in the line up . . .

Now it's the front double biceps . . .

The side chest compulsory pose . . .

The abs and thighs

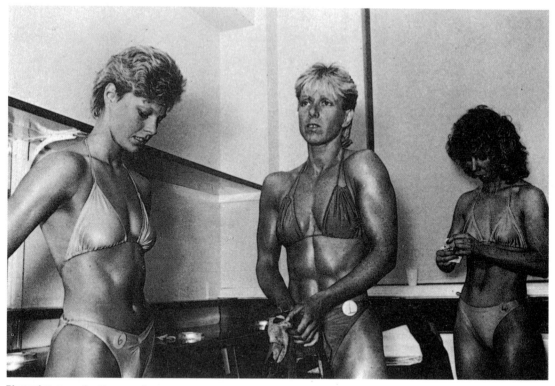

Please let me make the posedown

Adrian is shouting advice, but as the whole crowd is cheering Julie can hardly hear him. It's the front double biceps pose just as Julie has practised, then the side chest, back double biceps, triceps and then last of all the abs and thigh.

"Smile," shouts Adrian, and Julie remembers just in time to add a smile of confidence. Julie gets one more comparison and then they all go backstage. After two or three minutes the music starts up for competitor number one who struts on to begin her free posing.

All too soon it's Julie's turn. Julie is a final year Physical Education student and a good gymnast so she moves gracefully and poses well to the up tempo beat of the pop song that she has been rehearsing to for the past five weeks. It goes well and the crowd responds warmly. Then it's all over until the evening.

Julie and Adrian go outside for some fresh air but after eating some fruit and baked potatoes which Julie has specially prepared they return to the hall well in time for the evening show. This time the hall is packed. Outside some disappointed fans are trying to buy tickets by offering double their face value but no one seems to be selling.

As soon as the lightweight women are called backstage, Julie goes right away. She gets ready again, but this time the atmosphere seems more tense. The determination to win shows on all the girls' faces.

"Please, just let me make the posedown," prays Julie.

She goes on stage and this time just does her posing routine. The crowd like her and she responds well to all the encouragement, hitting her poses harder and holding them in time to her music. Then it's backstage as she waits for the top three to be called. It's Diana Defries, Frankie Hutchinson and Maxcine Mason. Julie is left backstage to watch the posedown, trying hard to conceal her disappointment.

The crowd are very partisan and cheer their respective favourites. Diana and Maxcine are close rivals and during the posedown crowd each other. When the dust settles, Frankie is third, Diana, second and Maxcine's pro-

nounced the winner.

Julie is about to accept defeat and start the long walk back to the changing room, when she hears her name over the public address system.

"Julie MacDonald places fourth and gets a special award." Julie hurries onstage before the dazzling lights.

Standing there waiting to present her with her medal is the giant figure of handsome Jeff Everson, husband of Cory, the present Miss Olympia and World's number one body builder.

"Well done, Julie," says Jeff. "Hooray!" cheers Adrian. "You'll beat them all next time round!"

And so we come to the end of Julie's first contest. There were lots of ups and downs but plenty of excitement. Perhaps at the beginning of all this you simply wanted a better looking, healthier and leaner physique. Maybe now you want just a little bit more . . .

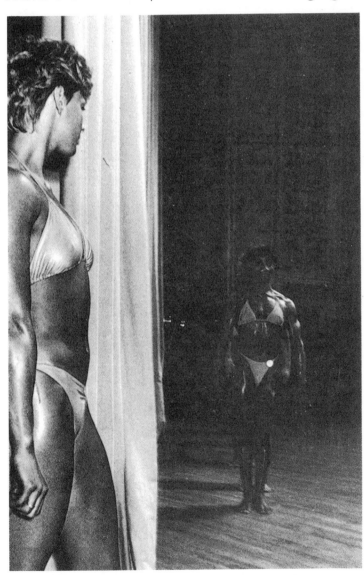

Ah well, perhaps next time . . .

No, I'm fourth with a special award from Jeff

You'll beat them all next time Julie!

Pregnancy

Though I'm not an expert, I do know many women who trained during their pregnancies and they were all extremely enthusiastic about the benefits they derived from the exercise. They certainly looked radiant throughout.

The strong muscles of the shoulders, neck and chest help support the additional weight of the breasts during pregnancy, and the exercises you do to strengthen the lower back will prove invaluable in helping to prevent the nagging lower back pain that so many pregnant women experience.

You won't need to change your routine except pehaps to decrease your weight as the pregnancy progresses and to avoid certain exercises, particularly the following:
Sit-ups, because they increase the pressure in the abdomen.
Leg-raises, not only because they increase pressure in the abdomen, but to avoid putting damaging stress on the sacro-iliac joint.
Exercises in which both hips are unsupported, such as standing leg curls and leg curls on the floor. This is because one hip has to support so much weight and during pregnancy joints are particularly loose and manoeuvrable because of an increase in the hormone progesterone.

Regular exercise will improve circulation and give you a sense of well being. You'll avoid the sluggishness that many women experience, have less muscular discomfort and gain less fat. And having given birth, you will soon feel like getting back into your regular exercise routine. Because your muscles are stronger, you will regain your trim figure very quickly, which has to be good for morale!

Holiday Exercises

I don't take holidays very often, but when I do I just look forward to two weeks of complete change of routine, with plenty of sea, sand and sunshine, and a relaxation of any diet restraints. This means I will be eating more fats in the form of cheese, butter, eggs and bacon and charcoal grilled red meat (and also, I must admit, large ice-creams, which are irresistible on holiday. We all have our little weaknesses!). It's not a bad thing to include some fats in the diet, as the body requires them to ingest certain vitamins, namely A, D and E. This is particularly important in hot sunny climates where the body produces oils to protect the skin from burning and drying out, so it does make sense to consume just a little more to help maintain our complexions in a healthy glowing condition.

As I have to reconcile my love of eating interesting and unusual foods and drinking local wines whilst on holiday with keeping in reasonable shape, my simple philosophy is centred on running to counter the effects of eating extra calories. During the last holiday I took in Lindos, on the island of Rhodes, I ran for eleven of the fourteen days. This meant a twenty-five minute jog up and down some pretty hilly roads at dusk when it was cooler. By this hill running and running occasionally in the sand, I found that my calves pumped up well and my legs kept in reasonable shape and tone. Walking also helped. The one definite exercise which I did was squatting, without using any weights, but doing quite a high number of reps.

I had to improvise to work the delts. I used cans of fruit juice in either hand to do lateral raises. Providing that these are done strictly with the elbows always above the hands and that the movement is slow and steady, it's possible to really work the delts.

By using a chair, I did a popular form of triceps dips which I supplemented by swimming using the breast stroke in strict style for at least 200 strokes, twice daily. I found that providing I didn't lose style, this pumped the triceps to good effect.

Then of course there were the abs. By putting a large towel on the sand I created quite a good surface for sit-ups and leg raises. A few sets of these, supplemented by crunches over a chair, kept my mid-section flat and in trim.

One thing I found most interesting when I went back into the gym! What had been most seriously affected by my lay-off was not a loss of strength but a lack of stamina for blasting through a hard workout. Even though I was really fit aerobically and probably able to jog further and for longer than I'd been able for some time, what I had lost was that special extra stamina which we all need for sustaining an intense training session with heavy weights. Never again will I ever under-rate the unique kind of fitness which comes from serious body building training.

Jon Conteh and I relaxing after training

Glossary of Terms

Aerobic Exercise
The word means 'with air' and is used to describe long-lasting, low-intensity exercise, such as running, swimming and cycling. Aerobic exercise leads to cardiovascular (or heart-lung) fitness.

Barbell
This is the basic piece of equipment for body building. It consists of a metal bar, about 60in long, collars and plates. The plates are usually fixed for safety in most gyms.

Burn
The intense feeling a muscle gets when it has been pushed to its limits.

Cut or Cut-up
A body building term used to describe a very well defined body builder.

Definition
A body building term used to indicate an absence of body fat in a competitor, so that all muscles are clearly seen when flexed.

Dumbell
This is like a small version of a barbell and consists of a short metal rod, plates and collars.

EFBB
The English Federation of Body Builders, which is the organisation affiliated to the IFBB that actively promotes and supports body building in England.

IFBB
The International Federation of Body Builders which was founded in 1946 by Ben and Joe Weider. It is the international governing body for the sport and has 125 national body building federations affiliated to it.

Pump
To 'achieve a pump' or 'get pumped' is to exercise a muscle until it is heavily engorged with blood.

Repetition
A repetition, or rep, is one complete movement of an exercise.

Set
A set is a group of repetitions, usually between 8-12, followed by a short rest interval of between 20-60 seconds and another set. Usually several sets are done for each exercise in a training schedule.

Spotter
A spotter is someone who stands by to assist you whilst training in case you get into difficulty, particularly with squats and bench presses.

Index

Page numbers in *italic* refer to the illustrations

abdominal boards, 99, *99*
abdominals (abs), *22;* exercises, 56-9, *57-9,* 74-6, 101
aerobics, 14, 15, 17
aging, 14
arm exercises, 48-55, *49-55,* 74-6, 101

back exercises, 71-6, *71-3,* 74-6, 101
barbell curl, 100
bench press, 20; machine, 86, *86*
benches, 89-90, *89-90*
bent over raises, 39, *39*
biceps, *22;* exercises, 49-50, *49-50*

cable cross overs, 92, *92*
calcium, 110-11
calf machine, 96, *96*
calf muscles, *22, 23;* exercises, 61, *61,* 74-6
calf raises, 61, *61*
calories, 103, 104
carbohydrates, 102-3, 105-6
chest exercises, 74-6, 101
chinning bar, 88, *88*
clothing, 25, *25*
competitions, 112-24, *113-24*
curls, 49-50, *49-50*

deltoids (delts), *22;* exercises, 37, *37,* 40, *40*
diet, 20-1, 102-11
dipping bar, 87, *87*
dumbell flyes, 46, *46*
dumbell presses, 35-6, *35-6,* 45, *45,* 51-2, *51-2*
dumbell pullover, 47, *47*

equipment, 24-5, 78-9, 81-99, *81-99*

fats, 105
fibre, dietary, 20, 107
front raises, 38, *38*

gluteus maximus (glutes), *23;* exercises, 60, 63, 66-9, *66-9,* 74-6
good mornings, 71, *71*
gyms, 77-80

hack squat machine, 95, *95*
holiday exercises, 125-6
horizontal leg press, 84-5, *84-5*
hyperextensions, 73, *73,* 98, *98*

incline leg press, 94, *94*
inner thigh firmer, 70, *70*

kick backs, 53, *53*

lat pulldown machine, 81, *81*
lat rowing machine, 83, *83*
lateral raises, 37, *37*
latissimus dorsi (lats), *23*
leg biceps, *23;* exercises, 66-8, *66-8*
leg curls, 67-8, *67-8;* machine, 93, *93*
leg exercises, 60-73, *61-73,* 101
leg extension, 93, *93*
leg raises, 57-8, *57-8,* 90, *90*
lower back muscles, *23*

menstruation, 21
metabolism, 102-3
mineral supplements, 110-11
multigyms, 80-9, *81-9*

nutrition, 102-11

partial wrestler's bridge, 69, *69*
pec deck, 91, *91*
pectorals (pecs), *22;* exercises, 42-7, *43-7*
preacher bench, 97, *97*

pregnancy, 21, 125
press machine, 85,
press-ups, 43-4, *43-4*
proteins, 102, 104, 107

quadriceps (quads), *22;* exercises, 63-8, *64-8*

reverse dips, 54-5, *54-5*

safety, 79
shoulder exercises, 34-41, *35-41,* 74-6, 101
shrugs, 41, *41*
side-bends, 59
side raises, 37, *37*
single arm rows, 72, *72*
sit-ups, 58, *58,* 99, *99*
squat rack, 92, *92*
squats, 20, 64-5, *64-5*
stiff legged deadlifts, 66, *66*
supplements, dietary, 110-11

thigh exercises, 63-8, *64-8,* 70, *70,* 74-6
touching your toes, 62, *62*
trapezius muscle (traps), *23;* exercises, 40, *40,* 41, *41*
triceps, *22;* exercises, 51, *51,* 54-5, *54-5*
triceps pushdown machine, 82, *82*
twists, 59, *59*

upright rows, 40, *40,* 100, *100*

vitamin supplements, 110-11

waist muscles (obliques), *22;* exercises, 59, *59,* 74-6
warming up, 26-32, *26-32,* 79